“Am I Dan

“You are, *carina*. Because you are fighting me with a woman’s weapons. I wonder if I should not concede you the victory now.”

“I remember when you were too certain of victory, Riccardo. Perhaps now you envisage defeat too easily.”

“I was not so much contemplating defeat as—honourable surrender. There will be many things between us—passion, joy, even perhaps love. Who knows? But peace—never. We were not made to be peaceful lovers.”

“Perhaps we weren’t made to be lovers at all.”

“You don’t truly believe that. Not now.”

LUCY GORDON
lives in London with her Italian husband and three cats. For twelve years she was a writer on an English woman’s magazine but left to be a full-time novelist. When not writing, she likes to travel extensively and go to the theatre as much as possible.

Dear Reader,

Silhouette Special Editions are an exciting new line of contemporary romances from Silhouette Books. Special Editions are written specifically for our readers who want a story with heightened romantic tension.

Special Editions have all the elements you've enjoyed in Silhouette Romances and *more*. These stories concentrate on romance in a longer, more realistic and sophisticated way, and they feature greater sensual detail.

I hope you enjoy this book and all the wonderful romances from Silhouette.

Karen Solem
Editor-in-Chief
Silhouette Books

LUCY GORDON

Legacy of Fire

Published by Silhouette Books New York
America's Publisher of Contemporary Romance

SILHOUETTE BOOKS, a Division of Simon & Schuster, Inc.
1230 Avenue of the Americas, New York, N.Y. 10020

Distributed by Pocket Books

ISBN: 0-671-53648-6

First Silhouette Books printing February, 1984

10 9 8 7 6 5 4 3 2 1

Map by Ray Lundgren

America's Publisher of Contemporary Romance

Printed in the U.S.A.

Legacy of Fire

AUSTRIA
SWITZERLAND
VENICE
Trieste
YUGOSLAVIA
MILAN
Verona
Padua
Ferrara
TURIN
Parma
Bologna
Ravenna
GENOA
La Spezia
Rimini
FLORENCE
FRANCE
Pisa
LIGURIAN SEA
Siena
Perugia
Assisi
ADRIATIC SEA
CORSICA
ROME
NAPLES
SARDINIA
TYRRHENIAN SEA
PALERMO
ITALY
SICILY
IONIAN SEA

Chapter One

"I don't know why the old man left a will like this," said Henry Barnum crossly. "For one thing, it puts you at cross purposes with Riccardo Tornese, and that's a prospect I don't envy you."

"Perhaps Alfonso thought I could handle his son," said Karen with a faint smile.

"If he thought that, then he must have been 'of unsound mind,'" said the elderly lawyer bluntly. "No one has yet succeeded in 'handling' Riccardo Tornese, and if you have any ideas of being the first, I hope you'll put them right out of your head. Even his own father was afraid of him."

"Alfonso wasn't afraid of anybody," said Karen. "He couldn't have built up a multi-million pound empire if he had been."

Henry Barnum put down the last will and testament of Alfonso Tornese, with its provisions that were going to set the world on its ears, and leaned back to regard Karen across his desk.

"And now part of that empire's yours," he said. "Just how well did you know him?"

"Pretty well these last few years. He lived with Mother

whenever he was in London. I suppose I first met him about fifteen years ago. I was only ten and, of course, I didn't understand the nature of their relationship. But later I came to realise that they loved each other, and we were living in a house he'd bought for her."

"Did you like him?"

"Eventually, yes. In the beginning I was young and inclined to judge harshly, so I blamed him for not marrying her. But Mother explained that he had a wife and three children that he couldn't leave. He had them in Rome and us in London, and after a while it came to seem quite natural. Plus Mother was happy. I could see that."

"People will say, of course, that you are Alfonso's daughter," Henry Barnum mused.

"Not when they've seen this," said Karen, and laid a photograph on the desk.

Henry Barnum studied it. It showed a man in his mid-thirties with dark blond hair and features that were just too delicate for a male face. Those same features were clearly visible on the girl who sat on the other side of the desk. She had the same widely spaced eyes and curving mouth. But they were off-set by a decisive little chin that gave her face a strength the man's lacked.

This was a weakling, the lawyer decided, a man who would run away when life got rough. Karen Conway would face it out. At twenty-five she had the look of a woman who knew where she was going. The man looked as though he had never known. Still, the resemblance was unmistakable.

"That was my mother's husband—and my father," said Karen.

Henry Barnum nodded. "No one could doubt it when they've seen this," he agreed.

"Besides, I was ten before my mother met Alfonso Tornese for the first time," said Karen.

"How did they come to meet?"

"She was a professional photographer. The London

public relations office of Tornese Elettronica Internazionale hired her to photograph him for their company brochure while he was on a trip over here. I think they fell in love straight away. Whenever I saw them together it was obvious that he adored her. His eyes would follow her everywhere. He cried at her funeral. He was such a strong man, so fierce and powerful that he made everyone afraid of him. But he cried."

"And then he went home and rewrote his will," said Henry Barnum. "This is dated a week after your mother's death, a year ago."

"And now he's dead himself," said Karen sadly. "He didn't outlive her for long. He said he wouldn't. The last time I saw him—it was only two months ago—he said, 'You'll get a surprise, *cara,* when my will is read, and it won't be long now.' I just thought he meant to leave me some money. I never dreamed of—*this.*" She made a gesture at the will that lay between them.

"Twenty-five percent of Tornese Elettronica Internazionale," said Henry Barnum. "And he no longer owned the whole of the firm himself. He'd been shifting shares to his sons for years, so that they each owned about fifteen percent already. Now they'll each have thirty, with the remaining fifteen percent held by his widow.

"That's put the cat among the pigeons and no mistake. Despite its size the firm has always been run as tightly as the smallest family business. All the seats on the board have been held by shareholders, which, till now, has meant Alfonso and his two sons and no one else. If you were mad enough to refuse to sell out, you'd go on the board automatically. You'd be able to combine with either son to defeat the other. The widow's fifteen percent couldn't affect the outcome."

"What on earth must she be thinking?" said Karen.

"I doubt it comes as any great surprise to her to know that her husband had outside interests," said Henry Barnum dryly. "Italian men usually do, especially at that level of wealth. They remain permanently bachelors—even when they get married, if you see what I mean."

Karen couldn't deny it. It fitted too well with stray scraps of information she had gleaned about Alfonso over the years. He had travelled extensively throughout the major cities of Europe, spending at least half his time away from the Roman villa that was officially his home, and wherever he was he had passed his time casually with various women.

This pattern changed when he met Sandra Conway. When in London he had behaved like the most devoted husband to her and declared that his adventures in other cities had ceased altogether. Karen, going through a phase of teenage cynicism, had tartly pointed out to Sandra that there was no way of knowing if this were actually true, and had received the reply,

"Not all men are like your father, darling. Some of them can be trusted."

"Can *he* be trusted?" the girl had cried passionately. "He's deceiving his wife with you. How do you know he isn't deceiving you?"

Sandra had thought a long time before answering quietly. "I suppose in the end it's a question of faith. If you believe a man when he says he loves you, you have to believe the other things he says as well. Otherwise there's no point in your being together. I have his heart. He would not lie to me."

Despite Sandra's confidence Karen had gone through a phase of being fiercely against Alfonso. But her hostility had faded in the face of her mother's happiness.

Then Sandra had died. And the man who had loved her had followed her within a year, leaving his will arranged in such a way that his 'outside interests' were allowed to affect his family—which was something that supposedly no Italian ever did. So perhaps her mother had been right all along.

"Why did you say that this will leaves me at cross

purposes with Riccardo Tornese?" Karen said curiously. "It seems to me that I'm at cross purposes with both sons."

"Technically that's true," the lawyer conceded. "But you wouldn't say so if you knew them. I know just enough to put you on your guard. Luigi is the younger, about twenty-seven, and a bit of a playboy. His main interest in the firm is as a source of money to finance his pleasures. Riccardo is a very different problem. He's in his middle thirties, and he's been his father's second-in-command for years. He fully expected to be in control when his father died, and this will checkmate him. He's not a good man to thwart."

"Then it'll be a new experience for him," said Karen wryly.

Henry Barnum dropped his lawyer's mask suddenly and leaned over the desk.

"Karen, as a friend who's very fond of you, I beg you to drop any thoughts you may have of taking this man on. You won't stand a chance. His one idea will be to buy you out as quickly as possible, and my advice to you is to take the money and run."

"I wonder if that's what Alfonso expected me to do?"

"I'm quite sure he did. This was his way of providing for you. The price you'll get will be, literally, millions. The firm has never been so strong. No one will be expecting you to take your place on the board and try to interfere in the running of things. You don't know anything about electronics, do you?"

"No. But Tornese isn't just electronics, is it?"

"Mainly. Everything else is subordinate to that or connected with it in some way. Do you mean to be part of the firm?"

"I don't know. I haven't made up my mind yet. For the moment I'm just going to accept Signora Tornese's invitation."

"What invitation?"

"I had a letter from her this morning asking me to pay

them a visit, 'so that we may all get to know one another and have discussions.' I didn't quite understand that at first. Of course I knew Alfonso had left me something, but I had no idea it was anything like this. Now I know the sooner I get out there the better."

"And stay with the family in Rome? You do believe in going to meet trouble head on, don't you?"

"Why not?" She shrugged lightly. "Alfonso had a saying he used a great deal—*nella bocca del lupo*—in the mouth of the wolf. What better place to meet trouble?"

Karen had inherited her London house from her mother. It was too large for one person, but she had mitigated that by turning part of it into a photographic studio. Now it felt comfortably right.

As soon as she reached home after leaving the lawyer she made herself a drink and went into her office. Five minutes rummaging around among her files found her what she wanted—every company brochure that had ever been published in fifteen years. She began to flick through the last one.

As she read, her eyes widened. She had known that the Tornese empire was vast, but until now she had never needed to concern herself with details. Italy, France, Germany, England, wherever in Europe the expertise in any branch of electronics was greatest Alfonso had pitched his tent, raised his flag, and expanded. The original washing machines and refrigerators now seemed unimportant, although Tornese still made them. But it also made recording equipment, owned a record company, and these last few years had branched out into computers and video. The brochure detailing the firm's triumphs and acquisitions had grown bigger with every year. Only one thing had not changed. The photograph that dominated the inside front page was the same one that Sandra had taken fifteen years before. Alfonso had his little vanities.

Karen glanced at the picture. It showed a man in his early fifties, with a virile peasant face, bursting with life and energy.

"What have you let me in for—and why?" she murmured.

Suddenly she remembered Henry Barnum's words about meeting trouble head on and realised that they had a familiar ring. She had heard her mother say the same thing often.

"You always rush out to meet trouble halfway," Sandra Conway had reproved her daughter lovingly. "Try to take things easy. Don't be so fierce. You only make life harder for yourself."

But Karen had never been able to take that advice. She was determined in everything she did. It had started long ago when she had appointed herself her mother's protector. She had been a young child then, but the instinct to protect anyone weaker than herself and challenge anyone stronger was already well developed in her. She could clearly remember her own rage the day she found her mother crying because her father had gone away. Later there had been a reconciliation, and the child had secretly despised her gentle mother for being willing to take back the man who had deserted her. Soon he had gone again, and this time there was a divorce. Karen had never seen him again.

Her mother had supported the two of them with her free-lance photography, and for two years they had lived hand-to-mouth. All that had changed when Alfonso Tornese had come into their lives, taking them over with breathtaking completeness. Where Alfonso loved, he dominated, and within a short time mother and daughter were installed in a luxurious house, and their money troubles were over.

Karen had loved Alfonso and resented him all in one go. She had loved him for his big, blustering generosity, the all-embracing warmth of his heart. She had resented the way he tried to run Sandra's life, even on the frequent occasions when he could not be with her. She could still remember the bullroar of rage with which he had greeted the news that she intended to keep on working.

"I must have something to do when you aren't here," Sandra had pointed out calmly when she could make herself heard above the storm. "I can't sit and twiddle my thumbs. I need work."

"Not that work," he said at once. "You do something decent, where you don't meet men."

"I'm never going to meet another like you, so stop worrying," she soothed him.

"You do something different!"

"No. I shall do what I'm good at," she said quietly.

He had screamed and shouted, stormed out of the house, sworn that he would never be back, *never.* He had finished with a woman who did not know how to behave, who did not know what was owing to her man. There followed a thunderous silence lasting twenty-four hours. Then the red roses began to arrive. Deliveries came every hour on the hour, until the place looked like a hothouse, and when finally he telephoned her from Rome two days later she begged him to stop. Karen never knew what else was said in that phone call, but her mother continued with her job.

Alfonso had yielded, but not with good grace. If he arrived in London unexpectedly he would demand that Sandra cancel bookings to be with him. When she refused, he sulked. At other times he would take her independence with surprising meekness. On one occasion Karen, instead of Sandra, turned up at the airport to meet him. He spent the drive from Heathrow to London in black-browed silence, but once inside Sandra's house he occupied the time till her arrival in cooking an exotic spaghetti sauce which he served up to her with a flourish. Twice more he stamped out of the house, declaring that everything was over—did she understand, *over?* But he always came back.

He produced his masterstroke on Karen's eighteenth birthday, when he gave her a magnificent set of cameras and lenses—the latest, the best, the most expensive of everything.

"Now your mother don't need to bother," he said hopefully.

Both women had laughed at his transparency, but Karen had made a mental note. Alfonso was the eternal Italian male. He demanded his own way, and his apparent generosity was merely another way of getting it.

At that time she was working as her mother's assistant. It was another three years before Sandra began to pass the reins to her. And even when Karen had become the 'senior partner,' Sandra never entirely stopped working. To the very end Alfonso could not count on finding her in when he called. He sulked and muttered about this, but more from force of habit than from any expectation of being listened to. And the red roses still came from time to time. The last ones had been his wreath.

Despite everything, Karen had found it impossible not to be fond of him. He was a big egotistical child, bombastically proud of his peasant origins and the bullheaded genius that had made him master of a huge industrial empire. Now he was dead, and she missed him.

Inside herself she could admit to a little tremor at the thought of going to Rome and facing the whole family, who were bound to feel hostile, despite the courtesy of their invitation. But to the world she would show no doubts.

Her eyes fell on an ornament that stood on her desk. It was made of bronze and depicted a she-wolf suckling two human babies. It had been Alfonso's first gift to her when she was ten. She could still hear his voice telling her the legend of Romulus and Remus, thrown into the River Tiber as babies, but saved by a wolf. They had grown up to found the city of Rome, and now the wolf was Rome's symbol, her statue was everywhere.

The wolf's mouth was open in a snarl. Despite the legend, she was not a gentle, motherly creature. She had suckled savage children who founded a cruel city where civilisation and barbarity warred for the upper hand. Karen ran her fingers over the gleaming pointed teeth.

"*Nella bocca del lupo,*" she murmured.

The following night she had dinner with David Brightwell. He was the editor of a glossy magazine for which she did a great deal of work, and for the last year he had been pressing her to marry him. She had procrastinated. She was deeply fond of David, and he was just the kind of generous, undemanding man she knew she wanted. Yet something held her back from saying yes.

As she had expected, he tried to persuade her to remain in England and let the whole thing be sorted out by lawyers.

"I just want to see the lay of the land for myself," she told him.

"I don't understand what there is to see," he protested. "They just want to look you over and intimidate you into signing away your inheritance on their terms."

"And you think I'm easily intimidated?" she said, laughing.

"Not you." He grinned.

"Anyway, Signora Tornese sounds a poppet from her letter."

"It'll be Riccardo Tornese who'll be making the decisions, and you'll find him a very different proposition," he said gloomily.

"Don't tell me you know him?"

"I know of him. Some time back the magazine did a feature on the firm—international empire, glamorous family, finger in every European pie, that sort of thing. I made the mistake of sending a woman to interview Riccardo Tornese. He simply refused to see her. She hung about for a week trying to get past his secretary and finally had to give up and come home empty-handed. I telephoned him, and he calmly informed me that he didn't talk business with women."

Karen finally found her voice. "But that's outrageous—that's straight out of the nineteenth century."

"I keep telling you, Karen darling, Italian men do live in the nineteenth century. Of course, a lot of women go out to work because they need the money. But if an Italian can afford to keep his wife at home, that's where he expects her to stay. He does what he likes, and she stays at home, looks after the *bambini* and doesn't ask questions. I'll bet *his* wife never dared ask questions."

"He's married?"

"He was. She died a couple of years ago. There were a few lines about it in the Italian papers, and a press agency over there sent it to me."

"What about the *bambini?*"

"As far as I know he has none. That's one reason why there's so much competition for him among Italian women. It's a bit like marrying a king. For them the real status comes with being the first to give him children."

Karen was thoughtful. She had known none of this. But Alfonso had preferred never to discuss his Italian family, so that was natural. She felt a rising tide of excitement at the thought of her coming meeting with Riccardo Tornese. Two people had now warned her against tangling with him, and that only made her more determined not to knuckle under to a man who plainly lived in the past as far as women were concerned. She was one woman with whom he would *have* to talk business.

It was a month before the formalities were complete. In that time letters flew back and forth between Henry

Barnum and the Tornese lawyers, until finally one arrived saying that if Miss Conway would arrive in Rome and establish her identity, she could claim her inheritance.

Karen used that month to set her business in order. She had a good assistant who could keep things ticking until her return. Jane insisted that she was capable of holding the fort with the help of a girl she had hired as dogsbody. Karen had her doubts about the dogsbody, who struck her as scatterbrained, but she gave in.

She dressed for the journey to Rome with special care, choosing a blue linen trouser suit that she knew would travel well. It also set off her slender, long-limbed figure to perfection. She could afford to dress well, and she intended to go among the millionaire Torneses looking as though she belonged in their circle.

Her critical gaze in the mirror had taken in her perfect peach complexion, red-gold hair, delicate features, and startlingly blue eyes. But she missed the very things about herself that others would notice first—the gleam of defiance in the depths of her eyes that a man might feel as a challenge, the sensuous curves of her mouth that added softness to a strong face.

The heat of Rome in summer blasted her the moment she stepped off the plane. It suffocated her while she stood in the entrance of Leonardo da Vinci Airport, surrounded by her luggage, wondering what would happen next. She had been told that she would be met, but not by whom.

"Signorina Conway?"

Karen turned and found herself looking down at a pretty little blond doll. The girl was a full six inches shorter than she and looked fragile.

"That's right," she said, startled.

"*Bene.* I am Giulietta Bonnicelli. I have come to take you home."

Giulietta. Of course. Alfonso's third child. Karen's mind frantically dredged up the few details it knew.

Giulietta was twenty-two and had been married for three years. That was all she could remember.

When they were settled into her silver sports car, Giulietta swung out of the airport with a screech of tyres. The needle climbed and climbed on the speedometer. Karen, closing her eyes with terror as they weaved in and out of the traffic, thought she had been forgotten until a bright voice beside her said:

"*Mea culpa.* Always I love to go too fast. Rikki says I must not scare people, but I forget." The car slowed sharply.

"Rikki?" said Karen.

"My brother Riccardo. You will meet him tonight. Also Gigi, my other brother."

"You call a man Gigi?" said Karen, bewildered.

"Of course. Is short for Luigi. Why not?"

"Well—that is—it seems such an odd name for a man."

"In Italy is very common. Everyone calls him that. But not everyone calls my other brother Rikki. Only me. And me not always. It matters what his mood is."

"And what is his mood usually?"

"Mostly not good. He works very hard, and that makes him cross and stern. He does not enjoy himself."

"He must have a great deal to do, running the company," said Karen cautiously.

A peal of laughter answered her. "But he does not run the company. He is only on the board, but he is not in charge."

"Then who is in charge?"

"Nobody, until they choose a chairman. And that they cannot do because of you."

There it was, the first reference to the explosive situation that had brought Karen here, and it had slipped out in the most casual manner. From the way Giulietta stopped talking abruptly, Karen guessed that she had let her tongue run further than intended. She looked at the girl and found her trying to take a surreptitious glance out of the corner of her eye. At the same moment they both began to laugh.

"Please," Giulietta said childishly, "I did not say that. I am not to talk of it."

"But I'm glad you did. I'm longing to know what everyone's thinking. The worst, I should imagine."

"Oh, no," said Giulietta, jumping immediately to the right conclusion. "My papa was not your papa. I know this. Rikki says so."

"And what does Rikki know about it?" said Karen, illogically nettled.

"Rikki knows about everything," said Giulietta firmly. "And he says you are not our sister. And now that I see you, I know it is true."

"I'm glad of that. I wouldn't have liked any misunderstandings. But doesn't that make it worse in a way? I mean, your father leaving me part of his firm and you—" She stopped, embarrassed.

"That does not matter," Giulietta said, coming to her rescue. "Everything Papa meant me to have, he gave me when I married, and that was my dowry. Do not be thinking of me as *poverina,* I beseech you. Papa said to me then, 'That is all, *cara.* The business to my sons. Business is not for women."

"But—"

"I know. It is very strange, is it not?"

Karen was saved from having to answer by the sight of a large neon sign, clearly visible a great distance ahead, on one side of the road. It read *Tornese Elettronica Internazionale.* As the car drew nearer she could see that beneath the sign was a long grey building on two levels. Then there was another, and another, until Karen could see what was almost a village of grey buildings.

"That's the local factory," said Giulietta. "It makes fridges and washing machines."

"Where are the others?"

"There is one in Turin that makes small car components, one in Milan that makes recording equipment, and another in Arella. There are other things in other countries, but about them I don't know so much."

"Aren't you interested?"

"Why I should be interested?" said Giulietta, confusing the order of her words in a way that Karen was becoming used to. "What is business to do with me? I have my husband and my baby and my home."

"Tell me about them," said Karen at once. This was safer ground.

For the rest of the journey Giulietta chatted happily about her husband, the wonderful Pietro, and her eighteen-month-old son, the wonderful Carlo, and her step-daughter, Maria, who was not wonderful and lived with them in their apartment in Rome. Superficially Giulietta fitted the pattern of the traditional Italian wife, staying at home to look after the baby. But it became increasingly obvious that both the home and the baby were cared for by an army of servants, and the amount of time Giulietta spent within her own four walls was minute. When she wasn't buying clothes she seemed to be having lunch and coffee with her girl friends, who all sounded as rich and empty-headed as Giulietta herself.

Karen found herself responding warmly to the pretty flaxen-haired doll. Giulietta was a sunny-tempered child whom it was impossible to dislike. In that respect she was exactly like her father.

They had swung off the main road some time back, and were now in the country, with grass verges by the road and lines of tall trees. At intervals Karen saw buildings which might have been mausoleums.

"We are nearly there," said Giulietta. "This is the Appian Way. Our villa is along here."

It became darker as the car swung away onto a side road overhung by trees. Some iron gates came into view, and beyond them a long drive, at the end of which stood a low villa. At this hour of the day the shutters were down. As the car glided to a halt Karen had time to notice that the greenery around them was dotted with statues, and when the engine was turned off, she could hear the soft plashing of a fountain.

The inside of the villa was blessedly cool. The floor of the hall was marble, as was the huge staircase ahead that led to the upper levels, and in two small alcoves, directly opposite each other, two small fountains trickled. Large paintings dominated the walls, and a brief glance was enough to assure Karen that they were originals, and masterpieces. The whole atmosphere was one of traditional elegance, based on extreme wealth.

Karen gasped when she saw her room, the biggest private room she had ever seen. The bed was six feet wide, with an elaborate carved bedhead. The outer wall was taken up with two French windows, which opened onto a balcony running right round the house. A door led to a bathroom made out of pale, dappled-green marble.

"It's beautiful," Karen breathed.

Giulietta plumped herself down on the bed and surveyed Karen.

"I am to apologise to you for Mama. She should greet you herself, but she lies down every afternoon to rest. She is not strong."

"Tell me a little more about your family, won't you?" said Karen. "How many of you live here?"

"All of us . . . sometimes," said Giulietta. "I live in Rome with Pietro, but I still have a room and clothes here. Gigi lives here all the time—officially. But he also has an apartment in Rome where he takes girls he can't tell

Mama about, and Rikki has a villa further out in the hills. He lives half there, half here. Only Mama and Franca live here all the time."

"I don't think I've ever heard of Franca before."

Giulietta shrugged slim shoulders. "She is a distant cousin of Papa," she said. "She has always lived with us. You will meet her tonight."

The maid appeared bearing a light meal of fruit, rolls and wine, which Karen consumed gratefully. Giulietta chattered nonstop until the maid, who was unpacking Karen's luggage, took out a floor-length evening dress made of pale yellow chiffon. Then she bounced up excitedly.

"You wear that for dinner tonight," she insisted. "Is perfect." She gabbled something in Italian to the maid who left the room with the dress. "She press it and come back later," she explained. "Very good. Rikki will approve."

"Does that matter?" said Karen crossly.

Giulietta gave a peal of merry laughter. "It matters, *cara*. You think you don't mind if Rikki likes you, but you will. Girls always mind if Rikki likes them. I go now. You rest."

She bustled out, leaving Karen alone with her thoughts, which had taken a turn for the worse. She had half a mind to reject the yellow dress so that no one should think she cared twopence for this man's opinion. But that would be childish.

She dropped thankfully onto her bed and was asleep within seconds. She was woken by the maid tiptoeing back with the freshly pressed dress. Her watch revealed that she had slept for three hours and that it was time to start getting ready for the evening.

A shower washed the last of her tiredness away. As the water laved over her she surveyed herself in the huge bathroom mirrors. She was tall for a woman, almost five foot eight, with the long, slim flanks of a racehorse and a tiny waist.

The cool chiffon made her shiver pleasurably as it fell against her limbs. It was a subtle dress, demure in the height of its neckline and the length of its sleeves, wanton in the way it clung softly to her outline—designed to confuse a man by its contradictory messages.

She surveyed herself in the mirror and an idea came to her, making her smile wickedly to herself. She remembered Alfonso's stocky build, and the tiny Giulietta. That kind of thing ran in families.

She rummaged through her shoes and finally located the pair she wanted, golden sandals with three-inch high heels. Now she was five foot eleven. That, she thought, would put Riccardo Tornese in his place. Not that she could think why she wanted to, except that everyone kept telling her she should fear him.

Giulietta came to fetch her.

"You are magnificent," she said in brisk approval. "Why was I not born tall? Is Papa's fault. Come down and meet my Pietro. He has come to dinner in your honour. Also Maria, my step-daughter."

At the bottom of the stairs Giulietta led her to the left and threw open a pair of double doors. The room was empty.

"Why do people not stay where I place them?" she said crossly. "Excuse. I find Pietro."

She bustled off. Karen walked slowly across the room, hearing the faint click of her heels on the marble floor. Her eyes never left a huge portrait of Alfonso on the far wall. It was clearly based on her mother's photograph, which made sense. Alfonso would never have sat still long enough to be painted from life. She smiled up at the beaming face, feeling almost as if the man himself were here to welcome her.

"Nella bocca del lupo," said an eerily familiar voice.

She stiffened with shock, almost believing that the portrait had spoken to her. Then her head cleared and she whirled to find herself looking at a tall, elegant man, who was regarding her from the doorway with a mixture of admiration and amusement.

"My name is Riccardo Tornese," he said.

Chapter Two

She had known, even before he gave his name, that this must be Alfonso's son. The voice was the same, and even some of the features were similar—the dark eyes, almost black in their intensity, the high forehead.

But the rest of him owed nothing to his father. He was over six foot, so that even in high heels Karen had to look up to him, and he moved with the lithe easy grace of a panther. His face was lean and patrician, the cheekbones high, the skin taut. It was the face of a man who habitually held himself in check. Only his mouth told a different story, being full and sensuous, hinting intriguingly at a dual nature in which frequent clashes were inevitable.

She was disconcerted at the amusement in his eyes. It was not what she had been expecting, but there was also a wariness about him that told her he would not easily betray his real feelings about her unwanted arrival into his life. To do so would be to give away an early point in the game, and this man would never have won his formidable reputation if he'd been in the habit of doing that.

She realised that she had stared at him a long while without saying anything. Her mind was a blank.

"I beg your pardon?" she said vaguely.

"I said that my name is Riccardo Tornese." He advanced into the room and stood close so that she had to tilt her head back to look at him. She shivered involuntarily. He exuded a masculine vitality that took her breath away.

"But perhaps," he went on smoothly, "you were referring to what I said before. *Nella bocca del lupo.* It means—into the mouth of the wolf. I believe that in England you have a similar saying, 'in the lion's den.' You do not ask what I mean by that? That is because you are too intelligent to ask stupid questions. Truly, you have come into the mouth of the wolf, have you not, Signorina Conway? You have come to where you will find wealth, but also where you must know you will find danger. And for that I salute your courage. I also pity your naiveté."

"It is you who are naive," she said, recovering herself, "imagining that I could be intimidated so easily. Alfonso knew me better. Otherwise he would never have left me twenty-five percent of his empire and the power to checkmate you."

He gave her a cool, speculative look. "Truly you have courage," he murmured. "This will be a most interesting battle."

"*Bene!*" Giulietta's imperious voice reached them from the doorway, as did the clicking of her heels on the marble floor. "You have met. See, Riccardo, now you have what always you say does not exist—" her upswept hand indicated Karen's height "—a woman who can look you in the eye."

Riccardo Tornese inclined his head. "Almost one might think that Signorina Conway had arranged to be tall in my honour," he said chivalrously.

Karen's lips twitched with irritation and amusement in equal measure. That came too near the truth. Certainly her plan to put Riccardo Tornese in his place had failed.

But she had one more card in her hand, though she did not yet know when or where she would play it. Riccardo had taken it for granted that she spoke no Italian, and she had been too startled to put him right. In fact she had learned Italian with her mother, who had learned it to please Alfonso, who did not like talking with his woman in a language in which he was at a disadvantage. Her youthfully nimble brain had learned easily, and talking with Alfonso had made her fluent. For the moment she decided to leave Riccardo under his misapprehension. Who knew when it might be useful to disconcert him?

As soon as she saw Riccardo's mother, Karen realised who had bequeathed him his height. Signora Tornese was as tall as Karen herself, a thin, pale woman with a fine patrician face and white hair. She floated into the room on the arm of the handsomest young man Karen had ever seen and extended a languid hand.

"Signorina, my apologies for not receiving you, but my health forces me to rest. I am most happy to welcome you now. My daughter has looked after you, I hope? Your room is to your liking?"

Karen made the proper replies while her mind adjusted itself. For the moment she was obviously going to be treated like any other visitor. That was good. It would give her time to get her bearings.

The handsome young man turned out to be Gigi. Like his brother he had inherited his mother's height and her fine features, but his figure was more frail than Riccardo's, and his eyes were full of a dancing mischief.

Giulietta brought forward Pietro, who turned out to be a swarthy man in his middle forties. Somewhere in the background, gawky and out-of-place, lurked Maria. She was about seventeen and might have been attractive if she had made the best of herself. But she was dressed frumpishly and bore an air of sullen belligerence.

Whereas Signora Tornese, who'd had a husband and three children, managed to look like a pallid maiden aunt, Franca, the spinster cousin, matched the stereotype of the Italian mama perfectly. She was a large, noisy woman in her sixties, with a vast bosom and a brown face. She took charge of the proceedings as though she were the hostess, bustling around, giving orders to servants. Her greeting to Karen was candid and unembarrassed.

"*Buon giorno, signorina.* You are very welcome here. But you are too thin. I fill you up good." She grinned, showing gaps in her teeth.

"Signorina Conway is English," Gigi interposed. "English girls like to be thin."

"Then they are *cretini,*" said Franca, still grinning. "What man wants to cuddle a beanpole?"

"Englishmen do," said Gigi quickly. "They like English girls to be thin."

"Then they are *piu cretini ancora,*" declared Franca.

It was impossible to take offence at her. Karen found herself smiling in delight.

"I am glad you are not annoyed with Franca," said Gigi's silky voice when Franca had bustled away. He placed his hands on Karen's shoulders with the intimacy of one who considered himself already privileged. "Nobody ever minds what she says, and we all love her."

"I can imagine," said Karen warmly.

"She said Englishmen are stupider than stupid, but I think not." Still with his hands on her shoulders he allowed his eyes to rove flirtatiously over her form. Had they been alone Karen had no doubt his hands would have tried to rove as well. This man made love to every woman in sight as naturally as he breathed. He was charming as long as you recognised that it was only a game—and could play it on his terms. Karen felt confident that she could.

"I thought you were better acquainted with English *women,*" she said in a bantering tone that exactly matched his own.

"On the contrary. I have made many hasty escapes from excellent English husbands," he tossed back. "My friendships with their wives have too often been brief and rudely interrupted. You do not, I hope, have an excellent English husband?"

"I have no husband of any description," she assured him solemnly.

"Oh, Karen—I may call you Karen, may I not?—I am so glad of that. For you are one Englishwoman I wish to know really well."

They smiled at each other in perfectly lighthearted understanding.

Out of the corner of her eye Karen saw Giulietta hanging on Riccardo's arm and laughing up at him. There was a foot between them, and he had to bend his head to her while he listened to her chatter with an affectionate smile. Try as she would Karen could detect no sign of impatience in his face while he listened to Giulietta describing a shoe-buying expedition that could have no possible interest for him. It was obvious that Giulietta adored the brother who was so much older and more serious than herself, while her relations with Gigi, closer to her in age and superficially similar, seemed cooler.

Their mother, too, appeared to have established a different relationship with each of her sons. Gigi hung about her like a young gallant, paying her flowery compliments that brought a doting smile to her thin mouth. Riccardo made no attempt to emulate or intrude on this performance. He merely greeted his mother with a quiet kiss and gently offered her his arm to lead her to her place. But it was Gigi's arm she took, turning and searching for him with anxious eyes.

The signora sat at the head of the table, with Karen on her right, as any honoured guest would be. On her left, facing Karen directly, was Riccardo. And on Karen's right sat Pietro. Gigi was on the far side, next to Maria, who kept staring sullenly at her father and step-mother. Franca sat at the far end, nearest the door, from where she kept up a running stream of nagging to the maids.

It was Franca who made the meal possible, amusing everybody by pressing dish after dish on to Karen. The diversions were a blessed relief, for Karen discovered that the most innocent conversation could be a mine field. When Signora Tornese enquired politely if this was her first visit to Italy, Karen said innocently:

"Yes, but I've heard so much about it that I've always longed to come here."

Only when the words were out did she realise the meaning that her listeners might put on them. But the signora seemed oblivious and continued to chat casually. Only the mocking black eyes of Riccardo Tornese, regarding her from across the table, warned her that he was alert to every nuance. There was something about those eyes that seemed to reach across and touch her scorchingly. Karen felt her pulses begin to race. He was trying to make her nervous, but she refused to let him.

"I am looking forward to seeing Rome," she said, talking in a clear, determined voice. "I have heard it's very beautiful, and I made sure to bring my camera with me."

The talk turned to photography. Karen allowed herself to be drawn into discussing her work.

"You are very young to have built up a successful business," said Pietro by her side.

It was on the tip of Karen's tongue to say that she had only built on what her mother had established, but she checked herself in time and saw from Riccardo's face that he had followed her thoughts easily. She began to wonder how much he knew about her.

"I hope you will find your way to the Via Condotti, where I have a jewelry shop," Pietro continued. "My assistants will always have instructions to give you their very best personal attention."

This time Karen fell into the unwitting trap. "But isn't the Via Condotti very expensive?" she asked.

"It is the most expensive street in all Italy," Riccardo assured her from across the table. "But why should that trouble you signorina—now?"

Giulietta came to the rescue, demanding that Pietro tell Karen all about his business, which took him to so many countries, buying and selling only the best. There was a branch of Bonnicelli on London's Bond Street, on New York's Fifth Avenue, on the Rue de la Paix in Paris. Soon the two of them would take a trip to Amsterdam to buy diamonds. Pietro went through the motions of shushing his wife, but his pride in being admired by a girl young enough to be his daughter got the better of him.

His real daughter regarded the two of them with a dark, miserable face, which lightened only when Gigi managed to make her laugh. She glowed with furious resentment of the lovely young step-mother who had snatched her father's heart and given him the longed-for son, relegating herself to the background. Karen was amazed that the enchanting Giulietta hadn't managed to win Maria over by now. She might have started by improving the girl's appearance.

Giulietta may have read her thoughts, for as they drifted into the next room to take coffee, she hissed at Karen, "Do not, I beseech you, be blaming me for Maria. Always I am trying. Always I am ignored, insulted. Okay, I don't care."

The upstairs room where they gathered for coffee had huge windows opening onto balconies which overlooked the front drive. Karen wandered out and stood looking down, awestruck by the beauty below her. Discreet lighting illuminated the fountains and statues which glowed in the surrounding darkness. Once again she had that sense of unearthly peace that had struck her when she first arrived.

A cool, languid voice spoke in the darkness beside her. "You are admiring my garden, signorina?"

Karen half-turned to face the woman who had been Alfonso's wife. Her acute ear had detected the tone of the true artist seeking appreciation of work well done.

"I think it is the most magical thing I've ever seen in my life," she said truthfully. "Whoever arranged this was an artist."

She could just make out the older woman's smile.

"That was myself. Nothing is placed in this house—not a vase, not a picture, not a mirror—that I have not supervised myself. Not a blade of grass grows out there unless I have said it shall be so. This house, these grounds, they are my creation, just as the business was my husband's."

She regarded Karen with an odd little smile on her lips. "You are surprised that I mention him to you?" she said. "You are wondering what I feel about the situation in which we all find ourselves? That you shall discover. Sometime soon we shall talk, but for that there is no hurry. For the moment please believe that I bear you no ill will." She made a gesture that took in everything around her. "This house, these grounds, they were left to me exclusively."

She seemed to feel that this was a complete explanation of her attitude, for she floated away, leaving Karen standing alone in the darkness. When she went back inside the signora had seated herself on a sofa and beckoned Gigi to come to her. Her eyes softened as her favourite approached, but it soon became plain that there was a dispute between them. Karen edged nearer and heard her say,

"But you will surely honour our guest by remaining here tonight, my son?"

Gigi took her hand and looked at her lovingly. "Mama, I am desolate that an urgent appointment makes it necessary for me to leave this party, but that is business, I am afraid. You understand how it is?"

The signora gave a small, sad sigh and said, "Yes, I understand how it is."

Gigi looked up at Karen's approach and beamed. "And our guest will not feel neglected, because I intend to devote the whole of tomorrow to her. You will come with me, won't you, Karen? There is so much to see, and you must have a guide."

"I should love to," said Karen.

"And you do not feel that I neglect you if I go now?"

"Not at all," she assured him.

He was gone in a minute, kissing his mother on the hand and Franca on the cheek, blowing a kiss in the general direction of Giulietta and Maria that might have been meant for either of them, winking at Karen and cocking a jaunty eyebrow at Riccardo, who watched the performance unmoved.

"Perhaps it is as well, Mama," he said, taking her hand. "You should retire early. You know what the doctor said."

The signora nodded and allowed him to assist her to her feet. This was the signal for a general breakup of the party. Giulietta embraced Karen and announced that she would soon claim her for lunch. As the Bonnicellis were getting ready to go Riccardo moved towards Karen and said, "Perhaps you will allow me to atone for my brother's rudeness. The evening is young yet, and I know a place by the river where I believe you will enjoy sitting under the trees and drinking wine with me."

"Thank you," she said, surprised.

"We will go as soon as my mother has retired."

He escorted the signora away with a gentle hand under her elbow. When he returned a few minutes later Karen had fetched a wrap from her room and was waiting.

"My car is below," he said. "Shall we go?"

Like his sister, Riccardo drove a sports car, but where hers was a delicate, elegant affair, his was large and brutal-looking, designed as a display of naked power. He tossed his jacket into the back and drove in his shirt, the sleeves rolled up almost to the elbows, so that the brown of his tanned arms contrasted startlingly with the white of the cloth.

He drove in silence, his eyes fixed on the road as the speedometer climbed higher. Despite the speed Karen found herself at ease. This man exuded confidence. If he had driven twice as fast, she realised, she would still have felt totally sure of his ability to control the car. His hands on the steering wheel looked both firm and relaxed.

He slowed down as they reached the suburbs of Rome, and within minutes they were in the heart of the city, moving along the banks of the Tiber. Karen took a deep breath.

"Yes, it is beautiful," he said. "You'll see it better in a minute."

He pulled up in a side street and led her down some dark alleys until they reached a little restaurant. The tables stood outside on a raised island, surrounded by a line of small trees which were hung with coloured lamps. The chequered orange cloths were clean but shabby, and the place had a cheerful homeliness that surprised Karen. She had pictured Riccardo Tornese against a more sophisticated background. But plainly this was a favourite haunt of his, for the proprietor greeted him as "Rik."

Riccardo led her to a table under the lamps and steered her into a chair that faced outwards. When she was seated Karen understood. She had a perfect view down a short street which opened onto the river bank. Far across the river floated the dome of St. Peter's in floodlit glory. She stared, riveted, forgetful of everything but so much beauty. When she came back to earth she realised that Riccardo had been watching her, his eyes full of sardonic humour.

"So," he said as he poured the wine, "you have tried the first teeth in the wolf's mouth and not found them so very alarming?"

"I had expected them to be sharper," she admitted. "But perhaps the wolf thinks he's going to soften me up by playing with me first."

"Thinks?" He raised one eyebrow.

"He may find me tougher to chew than he has anticipated."

"Tough?" He seemed to consider the word. "Of course.

English women think it is very important for them to be tough. It is part of being liberated, is it not?"

"It's part of not being a doormat," she said, nettled by his amused tone.

"Did you see any doormats tonight?" he demanded. "There was my mother and Franca, both giving orders, and my sister, whose husband worships the ground she walks on."

"I won't deny that Giulietta seems to have a very enjoyable life but . . . "

"She certainly considers it so," he said dryly. "She is married to a man who dotes on her and spoils her outrageously. She has borne him a son. Her place in the world is assured, and because of this she has confidence."

"But what has she achieved on her own account?"

"She makes her man happy. She has carried his name into the next generation. She has achieved what only a woman is capable of achieving. You call this nothing? What can you show to set beside it? You have your work as a photographer, *si.* But even that you mostly inherited from your mother."

She stared at him, dumbfounded. "What do you know of my mother?" she said at last.

His answer took her totally by surprise. "I know that she gave my father very great happiness. For that I have nothing but admiration and respect for her."

She was silent. This was the last thing she had expected to hear.

"I'm glad to know you do my mother justice," she said finally. "But I'm amazed that that is apparently all you have to say about her."

"What did you expect me to say?"

"Well . . . don't you disapprove?"

"Of the dispositions of my father's will I disapprove utterly," he said in a hard voice. "But that is a separate subject, about which we can speak later. Of your mother's relationship with my father—there is nothing there for my disapproval. Such things have not been uncommon in Italy, where until recently divorce was unobtainable. And where there is real love—as there was between them—I cannot believe it to be dishonourable. It seems to me that I understand this better than you do yourself. It is *you* who disapprove."

She bit her lip, thrown off-balance by his ability to read her accurately.

"I didn't like my mother being a married man's mistress," she said at last.

"I said you did not understand, and now you have proved it. She was not his mistress. She was his English wife. Did you never see that in his eyes she held the status of a wife?"

"Aren't you angry on your mother's behalf?" she said curiously.

"Do not trouble yourself about my mother, signorina. She understood my father, and the affection they shared remained unaltered to the end." He lifted an eyebrow again. "This is a curious conversation for us to be having, is it not? I am defending your mother, and you are defending mine."

"I was really protesting about your antiquated attitude."

He shook his head. "It is not my attitude we are discussing, but that of my parents and your mother, who all came from another age. Certainly my mother accepted my father's infidelity, because she was born into a generation of women who regarded that as normal. But if my sister were to discover the same thing in her husband she would—you have an English phrase: Tell him which bus stop to use? No, but something similar."

"Tell him where to get off," said Karen, chuckling.

"*Si.* Tell him where to get off. She demands the same perfect fidelity from Pietro as she gives to him."

"And do you think she gets it?"

Again his voice had that curious dry, ironic tone that she

had noticed before when he spoke of the Bonnicelli marriage. "I am sure she does—if only for practical reasons. Pietro is grateful for the love of a girl twenty-five years his junior. He will not risk losing that love for the sake of a casual adventure."

"You don't like him, do you?"

"I have nothing against him as a man, but I did not wish him to marry my sister. I very much counselled against that marriage, but no one would listen. Giulietta is headstrong and demands her own way in everything."

"It seems to me that she had the right to choose her own husband."

"You echo her very words. I only feared that her reasons for marrying him were the wrong ones. I do not believe it is an accident that she has chosen a man old enough to be her father, one who is flattered by her love and will give in to her in order to keep it. Such a man makes her life easy, but for how long will she be content with an easy life? Will she not one day seek out a man who offers her the challenge that Pietro cannot? I do not wish to see my sister become one of those sad women who flit from lover to lover because their husbands can no longer satisfy them."

Karen sat in silence. She had been moved by the affection in his voice when he spoke of his young sister, and now she did not know what to say.

"But—" Riccardo shrugged and seemed to throw off his gloom with an effort "—perhaps I am wrong. Let us hope so. For the moment their happiness appears to be complete. Giulietta does what she likes with him." His eyes gleamed at her wickedly in the semi-darkness. "This is not uncommon in our country. In Italy, signorina, women know their power as *women*—and use it with subtlety and skill. Because of this they often become very powerful indeed."

"And I suppose you think that's fine as long as they're

content to be the power *behind* the throne," she said, nettled. "Any minute now you'll be saying a woman should know her place."

"Now you are putting words into my mouth, and I would prefer that you did not," he said firmly. "A woman's place is usually what she is clever enough to make it. If she fights a man with his own weapons she is *not* clever. She is throwing away her hope of victory in advance. No Italian woman would be such a simpleton as to delude herself that she could meet a man on his own terms."

"And I suppose you think I'm deluding myself now?"

"Your delusions are probably a little more complicated, and removing them from you without hurting you will be a delicate business. But I shall do my best. Believe me, I have no wish to see you hurt."

The patronising tone of his voice stung her to retort, "You can safely leave me to trouble about my own feelings. I assure you there is no question of your hurting me."

"Perhaps in this respect I am as old-fashioned as you have accused me of being. I believe women should be cherished, even when they are behaving foolishly. In fact, especially when they are behaving foolishly, for that is when they are most feminine—and therefore most loveable."

"The last thing I want is for you to find me loveable," she snapped.

He regarded her with a gentle smile, and a new note came into his deep voice.

"Oh, Karen, I could make you want exactly that," he said softly. "I could make you rejoice to be a woman and not regard it as something to be overcome, as you do now."

She was glad of the semidarkness, so that he could not see her confusion. The abrupt change in his voice had caused a little uncontrollable pang somewhere deep within her. She tried to fight it, telling herself that he was manipulating her for his own ends, but his sheer physical nearness made it hard for her to think clearly. She was intensely conscious of his brown hands resting lightly on the table. They were lean and powerful, hands that would be capable of holding a woman with great strength or great tenderness.

She trembled with an awareness of danger. Riccardo Tornese was a stranger to her, but this urgent response of her senses had come leaping at her out of the darkness like a silent-footed cat and seized her without warning.

"You are mistaken," she said in a shaking voice. "I do not regard my femininity as something to be overcome. But I do regard it as belonging to myself, and not to some man who's conceited enough to think I'm there only to serve him."

"Then you will never be happy," he said flatly. "As long as you hoard your womanliness like a miser you will never know the joy of giving. And a woman who does not give of herself and her love is not a woman."

"Then according to you, I am not a woman?" she demanded.

"How am I to tell? Perhaps there is someone in your own country whom you love? But I think not. Or if there is, you have chosen a weakling, or you would not be here. If a woman I loved wished to leave me behind while she flew across the world to deal with strangers I should . . . persuade her not to."

"In other words you would behave as though you owned her, as though she were a prisoner?"

His eyes lit up with something that might have been mischief. "Let us say that I would teach her to understand that her place was with me," he said provocatively, "and to be glad of it."

Karen took another sip of her wine, grateful that her

face was hidden. Her pulses were racing, something was making it difficult for her to breathe. With a few words he had stripped away a centuries old veneer of civilisation to reveal an instinct as powerful and primitive as the jungle—the instinct of a man to claim his mate and fight off all intruders. And against her will she was responding to it.

To her relief there came an interruption in the shape of the proprietor bearing sizzling pizzas, which he put on the table. He paid Karen some extravagant compliments in broken English, chatted with Riccardo and departed, sublimely unconscious of having shattered a dangerous spell.

Riccardo looked at his watch. "Excuse me," he said, "I must make a phone call."

He returned briskly a minute later.

"I had to call Franca to reassure her that we're coming back," he said, "otherwise she gets worried. She thinks I'm still seventeen."

There was warmth and affection in his voice. The charged atmosphere that had existed between them a moment ago might never have been.

"Franca?" Karen said. "Not your mother?"

He hesitated a moment before saying, "In many ways we have all had two mothers, and Franca is the other one. You must have noticed how she took charge tonight."

"Yes, I did."

"The kitchen has always been her concern. She mostly runs the house, too."

"Isn't it strange that she never married? She so obviously ought to be running her own home."

"At one time she was engaged to be married—for ten years."

"*Ten years?* How is that possible?"

"It is not as strange as you think. Franca comes from the South, from a very small village in Calabria, where everyone is very poor. She became engaged to a man who was a distant cousin, but they could not afford to marry. He went North to find a way of earning a living. But he was not just an ordinary peasant. He was a very clever man. He obtained an education. He discovered that there were things he could do. In the end he invented something. In order to find the money to market his invention he married his employer's daughter."

"And poor Franca had waited for him for ten years?"

"That's right. Of course she was ruined."

"But why? She couldn't have seen him for years. . . ."

"It made no difference. She had been his woman. No matter that they had lived hundreds of miles apart, and he had seldom given her more than a brotherly kiss on the cheek. She was officially his. So no other man could want her. Besides, by that time she was twenty-six—an old woman in the South."

"So what happened?"

"Her ex-fiancé was an honourable man. He accepted his responsibilities and offered Franca a home in his house. As the years passed he made a very great deal of money and Franca has lived very comfortably."

After a moment the implications of this sank in.

"Do you mean to tell me—*that the man was Alfonso?"* she demanded.

He laughed aloud at her outrage. "Of course it was my father. I told you he was an honourable man."

"Honourable? To ruin the life of a woman—two women, since he seems to have married your mother for her money."

"I can assure you that my mother does not consider her life to have been ruined."

"And what about Franca?"

"My father was a great man, almost a genius. He did what he had to do, and if others were hurt he did his best to atone."

"But he deprived Franca of the chance of having a

husband and babies of her own, didn't he? And according to you, that's the proper life for a woman?"

He spoke hesitantly. For the first time he seemed unsure of himself. "I do not pretend that Franca was not injured. I say only that he did his best to make it up to her. As for love and a family—in an odd way she has had those. I told you that she was our second mother. She has the warmest heart of any woman I have ever known, and she has been loved accordingly."

"But it's not the same, is it?"

"No. I do not say that it is. But the blame does not lie entirely on my father. Even to this day they are old-fashioned in the South. The women are expected to behave with the greatest discretion and to avoid unnecessary contact with a man unless they are going to marry him. It would be quite unthinkable for a respectable woman to be seen drinking with a strange man late at night—as you are with me."

"Even though our meeting is quite innocent?"

His voice took on a deeper, husky note. "Are you not being deliberately naive, Karen? Our meeting is not in the least innocent. In the sense that you mean, no meeting between a normal man and a beautiful woman is ever innocent. In this respect perhaps the Southerners are wise. Any one of them watching us this minute would know that I am trying to imagine you without that dress that so cleverly hides your body while contriving to emphasise it. That is a wanton dress, Karen. It tells a man that you might be available, but that he must be cunning to get you. It is intended to make him try to remove it, first with his eyes, then with his hands. No—" he gestured for her to be silent "—why should you wish to stop me when I am paying tribute to you? I am saying that you are beautiful and desirable, and if I had my way this minute I should be making love to you."

Without her noticing, he had slid his arm along the back

of her chair, and it now closed in firmly to the small of her back so that she could not pull away from him. She gasped and pressed her hands against his unyielding chest, realising too late what he intended to do.

"Don't struggle, *carina,*" he whispered. "There are too many people watching."

He drew her against him, his other hand behind her neck, his mouth seeking and taking possession of hers. There was no way she could fight him without loss of dignity, so she had to allow him to mould his body against her own. His determined, probing tongue found its way between her lips and began a skilled exploration of the inside of her mouth. Her hands were trapped against his chest, the tips of her fingers just touching the base of his throat. Beneath them she could feel a pulse beating madly. Something in that frantic rhythm told her that his control was slipping dangerously. This was a deeply sensual man, used to gratifying his body's demands at will. Everything about him told her that—the healthy tang of his skin, with its clean masculine smell of warmth and sun; the expert movements of his lips, which were hard and yielding by turns; the assurance with which he held her. He had told her in words what he wanted of her. Now his whole body was conveying the same message in a blazing communication that went beyond words.

Karen felt suddenly exhilarated. This man was dangerous, and she had a joyful, reckless urge to risk danger. Her head was spinning. She only half knew what she was doing as she moved her fingers softly against the throbbing pulse in his throat. At once he drew back so that he could see her face. A shudder went through him as he saw his own desire clearly mirrored in her widened eyes, and in the swollen lips that seemed to invite him to new plunder.

"So you are a woman after all, *carina,*" he said huskily, "though you try so hard to pretend you are not."

His hand was gone from her neck and was roving over

her full breasts, discovering them through the flimsy material with fingers that knew how to tantalize. The ache that pervaded her was almost unbearable. He pressed his lips softly against her neck, and her nails dug into his flesh as his mouth travelled down her throat, leaving a trail of little burning kisses behind it. He made a muffled sound of impatience as he came to the modestly high neck of her dress.

"That garment is a creation of the devil," he murmured in a voice thick with desire. "It is like a conjuror's trick. The real woman is always somewhere else, and what I see and touch is nothing but illusion. If this were not a public place you would not be wearing it long. . . ."

The words 'public place' recalled her to herself. In the ecstatic whirl of her senses she had forgotten where she was. Now she remembered and her temper rose. She was angry both with Riccardo and herself.

"How dare you make a public spectacle of me," she hissed.

He laughed softly into her ear. "No one thinks anything of it. They are used to lovers in this place."

"We are not lovers—"

"But we were meant to be," he said huskily. "How different it might have been between us if we had not had to meet as enemies. As it is, I must fight you, *carina,* and crush you."

"I will not allow you to crush me." As she spoke she pushed at his chest, and he reluctantly released her. There was a taut, strained look on his face that she felt must mirror her own. It was agonisingly hard to become earth-bound again. It was even harder to listen to the tiny voice of common sense that had not quite been snuffed out, and which reminded her that they were enemies—he had just said so.

Flushed, she looked round and saw to her embarrassment that they were being regarded with approval from the other tables. There was a little burst of applause as the proprietor appeared with a small vase bearing a single red rose, which he placed on the table before Karen, and another bottle of wine.

"Per gli amante il vino e sempre a gratis," he boomed cheerfully.

"He said, 'For lovers there is always wine on the house,'" Riccardo translated.

Karen just managed to stop herself from snapping "I know what he said!" In her confusion one thought stood out. Until she knew Riccardo better she must distrust everything he said or did. Above all she must hold on to the one weapon she possessed that he knew nothing of.

"And I told you earlier that we're not lovers and never will be," she repeated.

"I wish I knew the man who is your lover," he mused. "He deserves shooting for allowing you to roam about unprotected."

"I don't ask his permission for what I want to do," she cried, mentally casting David Brightwell as her lover—although aware that the title would surprise him.

"It is as I thought. You have done what my sister has done, chosen a man who is not man enough to offer you a challenge. But love is like life. Without a challenge it is without savour."

The fact that she was in total agreement with this had the perverse effect of increasing her annoyance. Every nerve in her body was jangling, and it would have been a relief to tell Riccardo "which bus stop to use."

"I don't intend to discuss my private life with you any further," she said bitterly. "It's none of your business. Do you think I don't know what you're doing? You're angry over your father's will, and you think you'll gain something by throwing me off-guard."

"Maria vergine!" he said in disgust. "Is that your usual reaction to a man who has shown he finds you desirable—

to accuse him of scheming to get your money? I will pass over the insult you have offered me. It is unimportant. What is truly sad is the insult you have offered to yourself. Have you no faith in yourself as a woman that you must seek other motives?

"However, since you wish to turn this into a business discussion, let us do so. I am certainly angry over my father's will. He must have been out of his mind to leave part of his business in the hands of someone with no experience."

"What about the shares he left your mother?" she said, trying to stop her voice from shaking. He had brought her almost to the edge of tears with his cutting remarks.

"They are to provide her with an income. She was never intended to interfere with the running of things. She understands this perfectly. I shall vote her shares by proxy. Yours I shall buy."

"Oh, *will* you? You're very sure of that. What makes you so certain that I shall sell?"

"Because you are intelligent enough to see that you have no choice. You know nothing about electronics or business of any kind on an international scale."

"Alfonso must have thought of that. Why didn't he just leave me money?"

"Obviously he wished to leave you a very great deal—far more than he could have raised outside the firm. As it is, you have an inheritance that runs into millions, but only if you sell this minute. If you start trying to interfere with things, I dread to think what the shares will be worth in a year's time. You'll get a fair price from me now."

"And suppose I don't choose to sell to you? What's to stop me selling on the open market?"

For a moment he was so angry that she thought he was going to hit her. Then he brought himself under control, but there was a taut, strained look about his mouth.

"You would do well not to mention that possibility to

me again, signorina. The mere thought that you should so betray my father's trust as to sell any part of his company to outsiders is intolerable to me."

"You couldn't prevent me," she cried.

"I could prevent you—at least for a year. This is a private company. No shareholder can sell without giving first option to the others. Effectively, that means me. My mother would not be interested in buying, and Gigi couldn't. He spends every penny of his considerable income. He could never raise enough to buy you out. The only person who could do that is myself. And under the company rules my option lasts for a year."

"And if you don't raise enough in that time?"

"Then you are free to sell elsewhere. But the situation will not arise. I will mortgage my soul before I will endure the sight of outsiders interfering in my company."

"Your company?"

"Mine by right. My whole youth was given to it. My father had no right to leave control in any hands but mine."

He fell silent, a brooding, stormy look on his face. She had the feeling of having stumbled on painful secrets. After a moment he roused himself and said, "I tell you this so you will understand from the outset how unwise you would be to challenge me. I have right on my side. I also have knowledge and experience that I could use to defeat you. But you will not force me to do so. You will be sensible and sell to me."

"I'm beginning to understand your definition of sensible. It means doing what suits you."

"I have told you that this is in your own best interests."

"And I'm telling you that *I* shall decide what is in my best interests. I have no intention of being bought out. I'm going to stay and take the seat on the board that my twenty-five percent entitles me to."

"You don't know what you're saying. You would be out of your depth at the first board meeting."

"I'll risk that."

He looked at her for a long moment.

"Very well," he said at last. "You must have your way. As you point out, there is nothing I can do to prevent it. There is a board meeting set for the day after tomorrow. We are to elect a new chairman and discuss various other business. You will be there, and no doubt you will make your presence felt in your own way. And afterwards you will come and beg me to buy your shares."

She lifted her head in challenge and looked him in the eyes. "I shall never do that," she declared. "Neither to you or to Gigi will I sell so much as one share. I'm going to stay here and be part of the firm—as I believe Alfonso intended me to do."

"In that case there is nothing more to be said," he asserted calmly, and began to rise.

She was disappointed at this muted way of taking her rebellion. After the fire that had flashed between them earlier it was the last thing she had expected. But perhaps he had finally accepted the inevitability of defeat.

For the return journey he switched on his car radio, which poured out Italian popular songs until they swung into the gates of the villa. Inside the house he bid her a courteous but casual good night at the foot of the stairs. He seemed to have forgotten everything that had passed between them.

In her room Karen changed into her nightdress and dropped thankfully onto the outsize bed. She was completely drained and exhausted by the day's events. It felt like a thousand years since she had taken off from Heathrow Airport, instead of only one day. As she lay there, her eyes closed, the sound of voices came faintly through her open windows. She neither shut them out nor tried to listen, until her own name caught her ear. Then she rose and went out onto the balcony.

As soon as she stepped outside she realised that the voices were coming from a room just round the corner from her own. She edged silently along the balcony until she was standing by the corner, just out of sight from the speakers but able to hear perfectly.

Manners be damned! she thought grimly. "If Riccardo Tornese is talking about me behind my back, I'm going to hear it."

For she had recognised his voice as she got closer. The other one was his mother's. They were speaking Italian. Plainly he was giving her a report of the evening's events. Karen smiled to herself.

But within seconds the smile was wiped off her face. For Riccardo was saying devastating, unbelievable words that made a mockery of her.

"At any rate I managed to discourage her from selling her shares. That's one thing gained," he said in that cool, maddening tone.

As Karen stood there, stiff with shock, she heard the signora's voice.

"Was it very difficult?"

"Not at all. I merely ordered her to sell them to me and told her there was no question of her being allowed any part in the company. That was enough to make her cling on, just to defy me. It was quite boringly easy."

"Do not be so sure of yourself, my son. I do not think this Signorina Conway is as easily dealt with as all that. I should never have let you talk me into sending for her."

"Mama, it had to be done. If she had remained in London she would have listened to lawyers who would have persuaded her to offer her shares for sale. And you know what a disaster that would be. I cannot buy out her and Gigi too."

"Is Gigi still determined to sell?"

"Totally. His gambling debts grow ever greater. Even his income can no longer contain them. I know he has been borrowing from you. I doubt you'll get it back."

"That is between Gigi and me, and no concern of yours,

my son," said the signora's voice, suddenly stern. "There is more to Gigi's determination to leave than just the need of money. It is a bad business when brothers fall out."

"And you blame me for that? Am I at fault because I object to his irresponsible behaviour? He wastes what our father worked so hard to build up."

"Is it your father's work you think of Riccardo, or your own? I know that in recent years you have come to feel as though you were running the company, almost as though you already owned it. And now I see you full of bitterness at the way things have been left. But I beg you not to let your bitterness come between you and your brother. He is as he is, and you are as you are."

"At any rate, I am not a wastrel."

"No, but you are other things that are not good. You have become hard and ruthless. And now I see you determined to drive your brother out of his father's firm to satisfy your own lust for power."

"It is he who wishes to go."

"But you do not think of ways to keep him. It is I, his mother, who have to do that. And I have thought of something. I shall come to the meeting the day after tomorrow."

Karen heard a sudden sharp intake of breath, then a sound as though Riccardo had wheeled away from the window.

"It was agreed between us that you were to give me your proxy vote," he said.

"I have changed my mind about that. I shall come to the meeting and I shall vote in the election of a chairman. I know you were expecting to be elected, and you shall be. But I am going to propose a joint chairmanship—you and Gigi."

Riccardo's voice came, low and inflexible with anger.

"I think you must have taken leave of your senses, Mama. You do not know what you do."

"I believe that if Gigi has equal power with yourself he will feel more inclined to remain. I shall take care of his debts."

"And do you think I can work like that—sharing responsibility with that playboy?"

"Is it only because you think him a playboy that you would like to see him go? Riccardo, I beg you, forget what happened long ago. The harm Gigi did you is far in the past."

"Not to me," Riccardo said violently.

"He was a child, a stupid, irresponsible child who did not understand what it was that he did."

"And do you think he is any more than that now? Has he not rather grown worse?"

"Riccardo, I am your mother, and I am asking you to put your ill-feeling behind you. I have lost my husband. I do not wish to lose my son also."

Her voice held a pleading note. There was a silence, and when Riccardo spoke again his voice was gentle.

"For your sake, Mama, I must learn to make the best of it, but what you have done is very bitter to me. I must take the vote as a foregone conclusion now. Gigi will probably vote for your plan, even if he still wishes to sell, so that he can enjoy making my life difficult for this last year. And Signorina Conway will also vote for it because I have angered her."

His voice came closer, as if he was returning to the window. Karen heard a note of grim humour in it.

"See what a rod I have made for my own back. Gigi will stay, and now Signorina Conway will also stay."

"You will have to learn to work with her also," said the signora in calm tones.

"I can bear that for a while." Riccardo's voice was casual, and Karen could imagine him shrugging. "She will be so overwhelmed that she will not seriously interfere. Within a short time she will ask me to take a proxy vote on her shares so that she can return to London and flee the wolf's mouth. She will soon take fright when she discovers how the jaws can snap."

"And suppose she neither runs away nor offers you control of her shares?"

Riccardo's voice floated out onto the night air, cool, casual, totally self-confident.

"In that case, I shall have to marry her."

Karen stood thunderstruck, scarcely taking in the little ripple of silvery laughter from the signora.

"What certainty, my son. How sure you always are that you can rule the lives of everyone around you."

"It seems to me a most sensible idea—the uniting of our two properties in marriage, to be passed on to our children. And children are what I must think of. If I do not remarry soon I shall die childless. That thought is intolerable to me."

There was a silence before the signora said in a quiet voice, "Perhaps Signorina Conway does not like you."

"She does not." Riccardo gave a short laugh. "She dislikes me a great deal after tonight. But she knows nothing of men. She is most elegant and sophisticated, is she not? But any Italian girl of nineteen knows more of the true nature of a man. At heart she is like a child, Mama. How easily she took the bait I dangled before her. I gave her an order, and she stamped her foot and defied me. I find her charming but predictable."

"But there is one matter on which you cannot predict her behaviour," said the signora in a serious tone. "Before marrying her you would have to tell her about Alicia."

"Of a certainty I shall tell her."

"You cannot know what difference the knowledge will make to this English girl. She may find Alicia impossible to accept."

"She will accept her, Mama, I can assure you. Beneath that defiant exterior she is more persuadable than you would think." His voice grew soft and amused. "Do not be concerned. The Signorina Conway represents only a very small threat, and one that I shall deal with easily."

Then he stepped forward and closed his mother's windows, leaving Karen standing alone in the darkness outside, shaking with indignation and wishing she could scream.

Chapter Three

The next day Karen's breakfast was served in her room, with a message to say that the signora never rose till midday. At eight o'clock the phone by her bed rang. It was Gigi, reminding her that they were to spend the day together and that he would be waiting for her at nine.

She had spent a wakeful night after creeping back to her room, stunned by the revelations she had overheard. She lay on her bed seething with anger at the way she'd been made a fool of. For the first time in her life Karen really understood the *vendetta*—the feud that never sleeps till a wrong is put right. The idea was as old as time, but the Italians had made it their own; their language had supplied the name by which it was known everywhere. If she did not pay Riccardo back in his own coin, and make him sorry he'd ever tilted lances with her, she knew she'd never sleep easy again.

With the dawn, some of her sense of humour returned. She could look back over the evening and see how naively she had played Riccardo's game for him.

I should have remembered he's an Italian, she thought wryly, and they're the race that produced Machiavelli.

Niccolò Machiavelli was the cynical fifteenth-century Florentine statesman whose essay *The Prince* had become a handbook for politicians and all men who wished to indulge in political intrigue. The Italians had embraced the character imputed to them by Machiavelli with enthusiasm. They were known for dealing with their opponents, not with brute force, but with subtle, indirect, but equally effective, methods. They did not coerce; they simply maneuvred; and just as an enemy was congratulating himself on having won, he discovered that they'd been holding the tricks all the time.

But I hold a few tricks, too, she mused. He doesn't know I speak his language, or he'd have kept his voice down. And now I know what he's up to—and he doesn't know I know. He thinks he's one move ahead, but actually *I* am.

She was feeling more cheerful with every second. As she stepped into the shower she smiled at herself in the long mirror.

"As for his assumption that he can marry me at his own convenience," she murmured, "it'll be a pleasure to disillusion him."

She had not the most distant intention of marrying Riccardo Tornese, so it didn't matter that he apparently had a girl friend called Alicia. But her mood darkened when she remembered that he planned to marry her and keep Alicia, even to tell her about Alicia, and that his mother seemed to regard this as normal.

I suppose she would, she thought as she dried herself. Alfonso told her about my mother. But Riccardo should have known better than to imagine he could treat me that way, especially after some of the things we said earlier in the evening. Well, he said it was going to be an interesting battle. He didn't know how right he was.

By nine o'clock she was in a confident frame of mind and ready to face the day in Gigi's company. She descended to find him waiting outside in his car. He cast an approving glance at her expensive, simple white dress and kicked the car into life.

"Why don't we change the plan?" he said as they drove along the autostrada. "You don't want to see factories. They're boring. I'll show you some of the sights of Rome, then we will drive into the hills. I know a place—"

"Thank you," said Karen firmly, "but I won't find factories at all boring. I want to see everything so that I'm well prepared for tomorrow's meeting."

"So-o," Gigi said, giving a long whistle, "you are coming to the meeting? You intend to be a power in the firm. How does brother Rik feel about that?"

"He knows my intentions," said Karen, choosing her words carefully. "I did not invite his opinion, not being interested in it."

Gigi made a little movement that was like a cat pricking up its ears, and Karen realised he had detected the undercurrents as intuitively as a woman would have done.

"You may not have invited my brother's opinion, but I'll wager that did not prevent him expressing one," he said with a grin.

"Well, my interest in the firm isn't welcome," she said. "He left me in no doubt about that."

Gigi gave a shout of laughter. It was a merry, attractive sound. Karen twisted slightly so that she could study him. He was slighter in build than his brother, with fine, mobile features. Her earlier impression of a cat was reinforced. There was something feline about the sinuous grace of his elegant body that seemed incapable of a clumsy movement.

Yet there was nothing in the least effeminate about him, Karen realised. He was that rare creature, an entirely masculine man with the subtlety and emotional perceptiveness of a woman. In short, he was dangerous.

She wondered what harm he had done Riccardo. Their mother had dismissed it as a piece of juvenile irresponsibility, yet Riccardo was still brooding over what must have happened years ago. Yes, she thought, he would not be a man who forgave easily, if at all. She was taking on a deadly opponent, but she was doing so with a high heart and confidence in her own weapons.

"So you are going to put brother Rik in his place," said Gigi, almost as if he had read her thoughts. "My best wishes. I have been trying to do that for years."

"With how much success?"

"None whatever. Riccardo steamrollers over me, and he always will. That's why I want to get out. I'm a peaceable man. I don't like strife. And as long as he and I are in the same firm there will always be fighting."

"Is that the only reason you want to get out?"

"I see someone's been telling you about my gambling debts. I wonder who."

"Not at all," said Karen hastily. She didn't want to go into how she'd come by that piece of information. "But fighting your brother doesn't seem an adequate reason for leaving the firm your father built up."

"You don't know Rik or you wouldn't say that. He can make life very unpleasant, till one is glad to get out. He'll do that to you."

"He can try."

"I wish I was going to be around to see this epic battle. But as soon as Rik's raised the money to buy me out I'll be off."

"Won't that take him rather a long time?"

"Not him. His credit's good. He's the solid, reliable one. I'm the black sheep. If I try to raise money . . . I don't say I can't do it. In fact, I've done it. But the terms are always hard. My reputation counts against me, you see. But Rik can walk into any bank and come out with what he needs."

Vicious resentment coloured his last words. But in a moment his good humour was restored.

"Are your gambling debts really that great?" Karen asked.

"Enough to make me need a large sum of money urgently. I'm already borrowed up to the hilt. So I must sell. That makes me sorry, for your sake."

"Why for my sake?"

"Because it will leave Rik in possession of fifty-five per cent of the shares. Nothing you can do will have any effect against him. If I'd been going to stay . . . Who knows? You and I could have got together to give him a bed of thorns, eh?"

Plainly he had no idea of his mother's plan for the joint chairmanship. But would it make any difference, Karen wondered, if his need for money was that urgent? Or would his mother once again come to the rescue?

"Well, you won't be leaving tomorrow, will you?" she said. "We might manage a few prickles before you go."

He gave her a quick, sidelong glance and a grin.

"How did my brother annoy you last night, *cara?* Giulietta told me that you went off together somewhere."

"We just had a drink and discussed the situation," she said primly.

"Ai-ai-ai! What a discussion that must have been! And now you hate him enough to spend the morning trailing round miles of factory. Well, here we are." He swung the car off the autostrada, down a side road, and into the grey village of Tornese Elettronica Internazionale. There he handed Karen out with a flourish. As they went round she found herself impressed. The village had its own clinic, its own shops—where food was cheap—even its own little church, with a resident priest. There was a bank where the employees were encouraged to lodge their money and received free financial advice and cheap mortgages. There was a small law firm whose charges were minimal. In almost no area of life did a Tornese employee need to look outside the protective umbrella of the firm.

"I begin to think I did Alfonso an injustice," said Karen as they went towards the main building. "He always used to say that he was 'a father' to his workers, but I thought that was just his way of talking."

Gigi gave his merry chuckle. "My father would turn in his grave if he could hear you say that, *cara.* He thought all this was a waste of money. He fought Rik tooth and nail over it."

"This was Riccardo's doing?" said Karen, astonished.

"Every detail. He spent six months in Japan and came back full of ideas about how the firms there look after their employees from cradle to grave. Rik's turned this place into his own little empire, and these are his subjects, bound to him body and soul."

Halfway through the first of the huge factories Karen's eyes were crossing with tedium. The building was airy, spacious, well-lit, well laid out. Long rows of workers sat at benches fixing small components together, to the accompaniment of popular songs relayed through loudspeakers overhead. It was pleasant enough, but the monotony made her long to flee the place.

"I don't have to see them *all,* do I?" she said in desperation as they left.

He crowed with laughter. "Poor Karen. No, you have endured enough. I shall now take you into Rome for some fun."

The city was already sweltering in its intolerable noonday heat. Traffic was heavy; horns blared. Karen took advantage of the delays to hang out of the window and look about her. It seemed that round every corner they came across the remains of a building that was at least a thousand years old. She mentioned this to Gigi.

"And tonight," he said, "when we go to Caracalla, you will see a building that is nearly two thousand years old—or what's left of it."

"What is it, and why are we going there?"

"The hot baths of the Emperor Caracalla. It was built as a vast sauna. All the best ancient Romans went there. It's in ruins now, of course. Every summer it's used as an open-air opera house. I have to go to a performance tonight to hear a singer I'm interested in signing for our record company. I'm hoping you'll come with me."

Karen accepted with enthusiasm. In this way she could avoid seeing too much of Riccardo at home that evening.

At last Gigi found somewhere to park the car, and after leading Karen on foot for a short distance he turned abruptly into a dark, narrow street. She looked along it and caught her breath sharply. At the far end the street broadened into a *piazza* with a fountain. Behind that row upon row of stone steps, flanked by azaleas, rose into the sky. At the top stood a church with two spires. Dotted all over the stairs were artists with their pictures and sellers of jewelry and small ornaments. The whole scene was a riot of colour and cheerful Bohemian life.

"This is the best way to see the Spanish steps for the first time," said Gigi. "The street we're in now is the Via Condotti."

Karen tore her attention reluctantly from the steps and looked about her. She had imagined that Rome's wealthiest street would be spaciously attractive, not this cramped little place. But the shop window displays were elegantly simple, and never, never was a price quoted. If you had to ask, you couldn't afford to buy. In a few moments they had reached a discreet jewelry shop where the name Bonnicelli was barely visible. Pietro came forward, beaming.

"Signorina, how kind of you to accept my invitation so soon."

Before Karen could gauchely blurt out that she hadn't known she was coming, a flash of inspiration blinded her.

"My jewelry collection isn't worthy of the name," she said truthfully. "I need a necklace for an evening dress. But I must tell you that as I only arrived yesterday I have made no financial arrangements. . . ."

Pietro interrupted her in a burst of horror. As though one would trouble about anything as crude as money. The signorina's credit was good. She could walk out this minute with the most expensive item in the shop. This was precisely what Karen intended to do. To wear something that had plainly cost a king's ransom would make it clear to Riccardo that she now considered herself part of the Tornese's world. It would be a shot across his bows.

She was whisked away into an inner room and seated. Champagne was produced and poured into a glass at her elbow. Discreet questions were asked. The dress? Blue. There were a variety of suitable stones. . . .

"Diamonds," said Karen firmly.

She tried not to let her eyes glaze at the selection that appeared before her as if by magic. She began to try them on, one after the other, lost in enjoyment. Gigi came in after a while and stood looking at her.

"That one," he said, pointing to her neck. She was wearing a delicate string of diamonds from which hung three larger stones.

"I thought so too," said Karen, pleased. "I wonder how mu—"

"Don't," Gigi moaned, one hand over his eyes. "Don't, I implore you, ask the price. The proper way is to wait until the bill arrives and let it come as a surprise."

Karen grinned. "I begin to see how you built up your debts," she said.

His eyes gleamed back. "How perfectly you understand me, *cara*. We should be married at once. You are just what I need."

"You'd find me awfully expensive," she patted the diamonds.

"Splendid. If you are building up debts of your own, you will not be inclined to nag about mine. Let us set the date immediately."

Pietro bustled in. When he saw the necklace Karen had chosen he overflowed with compliments and pleasure.

"I have just telephoned my wife," he said as he ushered them out into the main shop. "She is overjoyed you are here and commands you to come to lunch."

The temperature seemed to have risen several degrees when they stepped out into the street. Karen winced as she felt the heat of the pavement through her thin soles.

"It's only a few minutes away," Gigi promised.

The apartment was a section of a converted *palazzo* off the fashionable Via Veneto. The Bonnicellis occupied the whole of the first floor. Karen walked slowly up the marble staircase, gazing open-eyed at the magnificence around her. Giulietta was waiting to greet them at the top. She looked Karen up and down with speculative eyes, and Karen had the uncomfortable feeling that her hostess knew what had happened the night before.

This suspicion was confirmed within the first ten minutes, as they were sitting enjoying cool drinks.

"I am so tired I die," Giulietta declared melodramatically. "I persuade Maria to come shopping with me—no, I lie—I drag Maria to come shopping with me this morning. I spend hours trying to coax two pleasant words from her. It is for this I am weary."

She flicked her eyes towards Maria, but the girl was paying her no attention. She was sitting on a sofa with Gigi, laughing at one of his sallies. Her face was transformed, its sullenness gone, the potential beauty revealed. She seemed at ease in Gigi's company, flirting with him childishly.

"I suggest this, she is not interested," Giulietta complained. "I suggest that, she does not want to. I take her to Vito's for a pizza, and almost I am throwing it at her. That is a pity, forVito makes excellent pizzas. Do you not think so?"

"Me? I'm afraid I've never—"

"Oh, yes. Last night you were at Vito's. He tell me. He tell me everything."

Karen looked up to see Giulietta regarding her with an impish grin. To her annoyance she felt herself blushing, which made Giulietta laugh aloud.

"Do not, I beseech you, be offended, *cara,*" she pleaded. "Vito is an old servant of our family. It was Rikki who loaned him the money to start that restaurant, and he still takes a fatherly interest in all of us. He gossips like an old woman. We all go there to hear what the others are doing. Except Gigi. He *never* go there. He don't want Vito telling Mama what he's doing."

"But surely," said Karen, recovering her composure, "your mother must have a shrewd idea of how he lives?"

"She knows," Giulietta agreed. "I think she pays his debts, so she must know. But much she does not wish to know. Where Gigi is concerned she is blind and foolish."

"I saw last night that he's a great favourite with her. . . ."

"Si. Is true. Much more than Rikki. Is not fair. Rikki carry all the burdens, and Gigi is no good. But she loves Gigi best."

"Does that matter so much now?" said Karen. "They're not children anymore. Does a grown man care if his mother loves his brother better?"

Giulietta raised an eyebrow at her, and for a moment she looked and sounded uncannily like Riccardo had done the night before.

"Ah, you are an Englishwoman, *cara.* In England it is not 'manly' for a man to love his mother too much, *si?* Here is not so. Here a man is not ashamed to admit that he is close to his mother, that she can hurt him. And no one think him not a man. Rikki minds. He doesn't show it because he's too proud. But he minds."

Karen hid her scepticism, but to her it was inconceivable that the self-confident Riccardo Tornese could have a streak of such unexpected vulnerability. Giulietta, she thought, was being sentimental.

"At any rate, he has you to make up for it," she said. "There's no doubt who's your favourite."

"And you are puzzled by that," said Giulietta shrewdly. "You are wondering what I find in him to love when he is so much older than me and so stern and serious, and I have the brains of a bunny rabbit?"

"Well," said Karen, laughing at the droll expression on the other girl's face, "I wouldn't have put it *quite* like that—"

"But is true, *si?* Let me tell you, *cara,* Rikki has always been my father. When I am little my real Papa is always away. It is Rikki who mend my toys and talk to me, and tell me I look pretty in a new dress. And he protects me from Gigi." Giulietta cast a quick glance at her brother and lowered her voice. "Gigi is very spiteful little boy, always trying to bully me. But Rikki don't let him.

"Later, when I have boyfriends, he meet them and he say 'This one's okay. That one, I tell him to stay away from you.'"

"Didn't you find that rather high-handed in a brother?" said Karen, frowning.

"No, because I understand him. If Rikki love you, he want to look after you. And if you don't let him, he get hurt. Sometimes he go too far, and then you have to say to him, 'No, I got to look after myself.' But you must realise, he do it only because he care."

"I know that kind of caring," said Karen, thinking of Alfonso. "It can be another kind of tyranny."

The little blonde head shook vigorously, "No, no, Rikki is a *patriarch.* He like everybody to depend on him. Perhaps too much, but he mean it for the best. Did you not see the factory today, the wonderful things he's done for the people there? My Papa was a good man, but he never had the time to ask himself whether the people who worked for him were happy. It was Rik who thought of it."

"But did he do it for their benefit, or his own?" said Karen sceptically.

"What has Gigi been saying to you?" said Giulietta, with a return of her disconcerting shrewdness. "No matter. I can imagine. Always he see the worst reasons for what Rikki has done, never the best. But most of the people in that factory are women. You think they mind they can buy their food cheaply and from shops that are near? You think they mind there is a doctor there for them? You want to know the truth? Ask the factory manager about all the woman there who have had babies in the last five years. And see how many of the little boys are called Riccardo. That tell you."

Karen laughed ruefully. "All right, I'm wrong. I'll believe he's a saint if you like."

"*Maria vergine!*" Giulietta exploded. "*A saint? Rikki?* A saint is very dull, I think, and Rikki is never dull. But I tell you this, *cara,* always think the best of my darling Rikki. Because the best is always true—whatever it look like."

The telephone rang and Giulietta jumped up to answer it, calling quickly to the maid not to bother. It seemed to Karen that she was anxious to get there first. She was glad of a moment to mull over what she'd heard. She had an uncomfortable feeling that she'd been caught wrong-footed. Her annoyance with Riccardo had led her to accept Gigi's opinions of him without question, but justice forced her to admit that Giulietta's explanation of the factory-village made sense. It was Riccardo, not Alfonso, who was 'a father' to his workers. Giulietta, who knew him and loved him, called him a patriarch, one who occasionally went too far, but always from generous motives.

Karen realised that what weighed with her most was not so much Giulietta's words as the love that had shone in her eyes as she spoke. A man who could inspire such adoration from a scatterbrained younger sister must have some gentler qualities.

Giulietta's voice drifted into her mind. The room was so quiet that Karen could hear the low, urgent words without consciously eavesdropping. She found herself translating the Italian automatically.

"I had no choice. . . . Pietro phoned me and said they

were on their way and I must give them lunch. . . . What could I say? If I had refused, he would have been suspicious. . . . How could I explain? . . . Don't say things like that, *caro*. . . . Tomorrow, perhaps . . . if I can. *Si, ciao.*"

Karen kept her face carefully blank as Giulietta came trotting back, once more breezy and sweet-tempered. She had no doubt that Giulietta had been talking to a man, and that she had had to break an assignation because her husband had insisted that she offer them lunch. That might mean that Pietro knew, or at any rate suspected, his wife's activities. Whatever the answer, it looked as if Riccardo's worst fears for Giulietta were already being realised. Karen remembered the love she had heard in his voice the previous evening when he had spoken of his sister and knew an odd pang of dismay for the pain he would inevitably suffer on her account. Not that she intended to be the one to tell him. It wasn't her business.

Lunch was a light meal of fruit and salad, washed down by wine and black coffee. Between them, brother and sister kept up a running flow of banter through which their slight hostility toward each other made the occasional flashing appearance.

"We must go," said Gigi at last. "We have just time to go to headquarters, and then you must return home to rest, *cara,* if we are to be out late tonight."

The headquarters of Tornese Elettronica Internazionale turned out to be another *palazzo,* which surprised her. She had assumed that a firm which manufactured modern electronic equipment would have offices to match. But Tornese operated from a time-hallowed building that looked as if it had once been the haunt of medieval dukes. It was floored with marble, and above them soared high ceilings covered with frescoes.

"Don't be deluded," said Gigi, reading her thoughts with ease. "We have a computer, but it's kept decently hidden in the basement."

And Karen found, as she toured the building, that all the most up-to-date office equipment was installed, right down to individual mini-computers for the secretaries of all the top men in the company. Yet somehow the atmosphere of an ancient aristocratic residence persisted. And as they stepped out of the lift on the fourth floor to go to Riccardo's office, Karen had the sense that they were being led into the presence of the duke himself.

The feeling was intensified when she entered and saw him. His office was vast. On the far side of it, in front of windows that stretched from floor to ceiling, was a huge, ornate desk, behind which sat Riccardo. The journey across the floor to him was a long one, and as he regarded her from a distance Karen felt intimidated, as though she were being granted an audience with a great man. She suppressed the feeling firmly. It was too much what Riccardo wanted her to feel.

But his greeting was courteous, even charming. He treated Karen as a welcome visitor, asked about her morning, encouraged her to comment on what she had seen. He received her remarks with every appearance of interest.

"I have instructed the legal department to be ready for you," he said. "They deal with our family affairs as well as those of the firm, which simplifies matters. Let us see them now, as you can do nothing until you have officially established yourself."

The visit to the legal department on the next floor up was briefer than she had expected. She produced identification, including her passport, and signed papers. And she had the odd feeling that it was Riccardo Tornese's acceptance of her rather than any official stamp in a passport that had induced the lawyers to cut the formalities to a minimum. This was a man whose word was law in his own kingdom. She left the legal department a fabulously wealthy woman.

Back in Riccardo's office she drank the coffee that had been made for her by his secretary, a middle-aged woman in a dark dress. Riccardo spoke to the secretary in English.

"Lisa, will you be so good as to fetch the dossier I prepared for Signorina Conway?" When the woman had gone he smiled at Karen. "Knowing your wish to play a full part in the running of the firm I have assembled some papers that I think you will find useful. They cover the matters to be discussed in tomorrow's meeting. I advise you to study them thoroughly."

"But not so thoroughly that you have no time for fun," said Gigi. He looked alarmed as Lisa reappeared with the bulky dossier. "Karen will never have time to read all that. We are going out tonight."

"You should not be, either of you," said Riccardo curtly. "This meeting is important, and you should both arrive well-informed."

"I appreciate your concern," said Karen in a honeyed voice. "But please, neither of you worry about me. I shall have plenty of time to read what is necessary."

Gigi bent low and hissed dramatically in her ear. "Never fear, *cara,* when we are married no one shall trouble you."

"Perhaps you could entertain us with your jokes another time," said Riccardo with an expression of distaste. "I am rather busy this afternoon."

"But this is no joke," persisted Gigi. "I have already asked and been accepted, have I not, *cara?*"

"I definitely remember your saying we should be married, " Karen said, playing up to him. She had not missed the slight tautening of Riccardo's face. "But I cannot remember my reply."

"Of a certainty you said yes. We had only to fix the date."

"Then let us go and fix it, and leave Riccardo to his work."

"Do not forget to take your papers," said Riccardo as

she rose. "I appreciate that it is a bore, but I'm afraid it is one of the penalties of being a high-powered business-woman."

He looked up at her as he spoke, and instead of the derision she had expected to see in his eyes there was only genuine amusement, even warmth. She gathered the file and fled for safety, feeling that Riccardo Tornese could be disastrously engaging when he set his mind to it.

But on the drive home she recovered her equanimity and got her battle colours in order. A quick glance through the file revealed that, as she had expected, every word of it was in Italian.

Chapter Four

The opera didn't start until 9, so Karen had time for a long siesta. After a good sleep she rose refreshed and put in a couple of hours work reading the dossier. Most of the material was concerned with a large stretch of land just outside Milan, which Tornese Elettronica was negotiating to buy. Karen read the report assessing the land's suitability for building factories, its distance from the nearest transport, etc. Then she lay back on her bed, searching for a memory that taunted her with its elusiveness. It was something Alfonso had said many years ago. As a rule he had not discussed business with his 'English family,' but this time he'd been too furious to keep his thoughts to himself.

"Imbeciles—morons—see what happens the minute I turn my back. How many palms shall I have to grease to get us out of this one? And where the hell is Innoccino, anyway?"

Now Karen picked up her bedside telephone and called David Brightwell in England.

"I thought they'd have thrown you to the lions in the Coliseum by now," his voice came over the miles.

"They're not lions, they're wolves," she assured him.

"And I'm learning that there is a way to go into the mouth of the wolf and come out safely—if you'll help me."

"Say the word and I'll be there."

"Waving a sword in my defence? Bless you, but what I need is some help from your files—something that happened to Tornese about ten or twelve years ago. . . ."

When she had finished talking he gave a low, horrified whistle. "If you're going to throw *that* up in Riccardo Tornese's face, you won't just need a sword to defend yourself. More like a few tanks and a regiment."

She chuckled. "I'll take my chances."

When she called him back half an hour later he had some of the information.

"But not all," he warned her. "The firm did what it could to keep the details quiet at the time, but some of them leaked out. Here's what I've got. . . ."

When he'd finished reading it out to her, he said, "I take it this means you're involving yourself in the firm?"

"It does for the moment." She was reluctant to say more.

"I wish you wouldn't. I miss you."

"I miss you, too," she said, and immediately felt guilty.

When she had replaced the receiver she lay back on the bed, realising that, whatever happened, her relationship with David had irrevocably changed. For in his arms she had never known the riotous excitement she had shared for a few incredible moments with Riccardo Tornese. With unerring skill Riccardo had pinpointed the vital difference between David and himself: David offered her no challenge. With Riccardo the challenge was intoxicating and impossible to refuse. There was no turning back now.

Her gaze fell on the notes she had made from David's information. As she read them through her eyes began to dance. Riccardo's dismissal of her as "charming but predictable" was about to rebound on him.

She jotted down a few more thoughts. Then she closed

her eyes again and slept the sleep of the just for another hour. She was smiling as she slept.

At eight o'clock she went downstairs and found Gigi and his mother in the big front room. They were sitting beneath Alfonso's portrait and talking earnestly. Karen hesitated on the threshold, but the signora rose and embraced her graciously.

"I am glad to see that my son takes care of you. You look delightful."

Her eyes flickered over Karen, taking in the deep blue dress with the low neckline and the diamond necklace.

"Charming. And so right of you to dress for the occasion. Caracalla is, after all, an opera house, despite the hot dogs." She drifted away.

"Did I hear right?" said Karen, bewildered. "Did your mother say *hot dogs?*"

"Certainly. I shall buy you one. We shall not eat properly until after the performance."

"But I can't wear diamonds and eat hot dogs."

"Why not? Everyone else does."

Karen began to laugh. Gigi joined in, taking her hand, while his eyes made caressing love to her. She was going to enjoy the evening, she decided. She was in no danger of falling in love with Gigi, but he was an ideal companion.

She was enchanted by Caracalla. Where once hundreds of ancient Romans had relaxed in the steamy heat, now only a few lumps of ruined masonry stood. But those lumps were vast. They formed pillars eighty feet high that reared up into the twilight sky. Floodlights played on them, giving them an eerie look. Between two of them had been built the biggest stage Karen had ever seen.

The opera was *Aïda,* chosen because its triumphal procession scene made use of the stage's size. Karen realised that her jaw was dropping like a little girl's at her first circus as horses, camels and even elephants streamed across the stage.

"Most people come to Caracalla for the spectacle rather

than the singing," said Gigi when the scene was over and the applause had died down. "You get a lot of young, promising singers just starting their careers. And sometimes I can spot them and sign them up before anyone else. Watch for him. . . ."

He pointed to a name in the programme. Karen tried to pronounce it and failed.

"He's Bulgarian," said Gigi. "No one has ever heard of him. The next scene's his big one. If he sings it as well as I think he's going to . . ."

In the next scene she concentrated on listening to the Bulgarian. She liked his voice but couldn't tell if it was exceptional. Gigi had no doubts.

"Come on." He grabbed her hand the moment the scene ended. "Let's get backstage and talk to him."

He threaded his way expertly between the ruins till he reached the part that did duty as backstage. The Bulgarian knew little Italian, so the conversation was conducted in English. Listening in silence Karen was astonished by Gigi, who talked like a man of sense and sound business instincts. The flippant playboy had temporarily vanished. Somewhere along the line the best of Gigi had got twisted out of its natural direction. She wondered how it had happened.

On the way back to their seats he bought her a hot dog (her second) from one of the stalls that were everywhere, plus a bottle of wine and two plastic cups.

"We've just time for a picnic before the last act," he said. "I'm feeling pleased with myself. I've got him on first-rate terms."

"Even I could tell that wasn't a very good deal you were offering him," she said.

"It was good for the company. When he's in demand all over the world, he'll be ours."

"But you won't be here to see the result of your labours. You're leaving the firm."

"Ah. . . ." He was silent for a minute. "I may be changing my plans. We'll see."

Karen remembered how he had been deep in conversation with his mother that evening. The signora must have told him of her idea, and it had given him second thoughts.

It was past midnight when the opera ended.

"The evening is just beginning," said Gigi as they made their way to the car. "I'm going to buy you supper at a little club I know."

He drove with the top of his car down, so that she had an uninterrupted view of the city, most of which was floodlit. Palaces, churches, fountains, monuments, all seemed to float out of the darkness at her, then float away again. She felt serenely relaxed and happy.

In a few minutes they were in the heart of the city, driving down the Via Veneto. It was still a blaze of light with its all-night cafés stretched across the wide pavements. At the bottom of the street Gigi swerved so that they passed the Tornese offices, which still had some lights on. Karen wondered where Riccardo was now. Was he in his office, making plans for the next day's meeting? Was he at home, making a last-minute attempt to change his mother's mind? Or was he out somewhere with the mysterious Alicia?

She realised that she had managed to avoid thinking of Alicia for most of the day, although the rest of the conversation had run through her mind many times. But now Alicia would not be shut out. Whoever she was she obviously had Riccardo's love, and he was planning to keep her in his life, while marrying Karen for her money. Why should she be surprised at that? Wasn't it much the same as his father had done?

Probably he was with her now, kissing her as he had kissed Karen the night before. But this time it would be different. It would be a kiss of love and tenderness, not part of a cynical game in which passion was merely one of the counters. And she would react—how? What sort of woman was Alicia that she had snared Riccardo's heart?

"Don't twist your necklace like that," said Gigi. "You'll break it."

Karen snatched her hand away, and felt it seized between his warm, strong ones.

"You're shaking, *cara.* What's the matter?"

"I'm just hungry," she managed to say. "Hot dogs aren't very filling."

"Well, we're here now. You can have some supper."

"We've stopped," she said in surprise. The car was standing in a dark side road, the engine switched off. She had no recollection of it happening.

"We stopped a couple of minutes ago," he chided her. "You were in a private dreamworld. I wish I knew what you were thinking."

She pulled herself together and gave him a flirtatious smile. "I may tell you later," she teased.

"I'll count on it."

As soon as they sat down at their table Gigi ordered champagne.

"Tonight we celebrate," he said. "Perhaps I will not leave the firm after all. At the meeting tomorrow my mother will propose that Riccardo and I share the position of chairman. It's worth a try. Of course," he looked at her, elaborately casual, "it all depends on you. Rik will vote for himself. My mother and I will vote for the joint arrangement. But you—who will you vote for?"

It was on the tip of her tongue to tell him that she would support his mother's proposal, but at the last minute she shied away from this attempt to pin her down.

"Wait and see," she teased. "Perhaps I shall decide that I'm too much afraid of your brother to vote against him."

"I do not think you are a woman to be frightened, *cara.* I shall await your decision with impatience—but without too much apprehension." He filled her glass and added,

"If I really believed that you feared Rik I should advise you not to let him know it, at any price. He likes people to be afraid. In that he is like our father. But I forget—you knew my father well."

"I know he liked to have his own way, and there were storms if he didn't get it," she said with a smile of reminiscence.

"Rik also likes to have his own way. But if he doesn't get it there are no storms. He simply manipulates behind the scenes, so that you end up doing what he wants."

Karen nodded. She knew exactly what Gigi was talking about.

"Were you actually afraid of Alfonso?" she asked.

He was silent for a moment, then answered seriously, "If I had not been afraid of him, I should not be here now. I should be on the stage. You might even have seen me at Caracalla tonight."

"You mean, you wanted to be an opera singer?"

"I wanted it with all my heart. It is the only thing I have ever really wanted. But my father would not hear of it. He started out as a peasant and built himself up. He was ambitious for his sons to become great men, men of power and influence in the world. And a man does not achieve power and influence by strutting about on a stage wearing makeup and tights. That was what he said." Gigi's voice had become soft and venomous.

"But your mother . . . didn't she support you?"

"In this one thing, no. My mother comes from a great family—a minor branch, it's true, and they were very much down in the world, but a great family, nonetheless. She wanted to see me on the stage no more than my father did. So now—" he shrugged "—I am what I am. I live in a world I hate, and sometimes I wonder why I don't just get out and leave it all to Rik, as he would like. Do you know," he said, turning on her suddenly, "Rik was the one who supported me. He told Papa I should be allowed to do as I like. And why? Because that way he could get rid of me. I told you, Rik's clever about how he gets his own way."

"You don't know that," she pointed out. "He might have honestly sympathised with you."

"*Cara,* let me tell you something that will be a useful weapon in your fight with my brother. Rik never does anything for anybody except himself. When he really seems to be considering your interests, that is when you should look at him most closely and ask what he is getting out of it."

The waiter arrived to serve them, and abruptly Gigi changed the subject. For the rest of the evening he was the perfect host.

"What are you going to do in Rome?" he asked while they were sipping liqueurs. "I mean, apart from the firm. That will not take all your time. How will you live?"

"I hadn't thought . . ."

"You will need an apartment, of course. You will never be independent in our house. As it happens, I know of a suitable place. . . ."

"Near your own?" she asked with a twitch of the lips.

"In the very same building. I think we should get to know each other, *cara.*" He stroked her cheek with a gentle finger. "You need someone to take care of you in this wicked city, someone to protect you from my brother."

"If I need protecting, Gigi, I'll call on you. But I have weapons of my own."

He looked at her, his head on one side. "Something I don't know about?"

"Something you don't know about."

"And you're not going to tell me?"

She shook her head. Gigi was charming, but he couldn't charm her into trusting him.

"*Bene.* I will say no more." He lifted his glass in salute.

Her watch showed three in the morning. When Gigi

rose to leave, she expected him to head for the street. Instead he drew her through another door.

"We depart in half an hour, I promise," he said. "But first . . ."

When she saw where he had taken her, Karen began to understand. The club was actually a gambling establishment. In the room where they were standing every game of chance was played. A roulette wheel was in the centre.

"Half an hour," Gigi repeated. "I have a feeling that you will bring me luck."

She did not bring him luck. They remained for an hour, and in that time she saw him lose an amount of money that made her throat go dry. He was transformed. His gaiety fell away, leaving him tense, silent, watching the table with burning eyes like a man in a trance. When at last she pulled firmly on his sleeve and announced her intention of going, he seemed to become aware of her with an effort.

"Yes, let us go," he said in a chill, thin voice.

In the car outside he sat for a long moment, making no move to start the engine.

"You are shocked," he said at last. "This is how it is with me. I do not know what happens, but once I start I can't stop. Do not blame me."

"I don't blame you," she said gently. "I think it is a kind of sickness."

He shrugged. "*Si.* You can give it a name if you like. What use is that? It does not help me."

"But you can be cured," she pleaded, "if you want to."

He gave her a dreadful smile. "But I don't want to," he said simply.

Without another word he started the car. He didn't speak again all the way home. When he finally switched off the engine in front of the Tornese villa, he turned, and she saw that he was himself again.

"Please forget what you saw tonight, Karen. I didn't mean to spoil your evening."

He helped her out and led the way inside the house. As

soon as the front door had closed behind them, leaving them in the darkness of the hall, he put his arms round her and drew her against him with practised ease. She relaxed, letting him take her mouth with lips whose movements were smooth and glib.

It was warm and sweet in his arms, but there was no riotous surge of feeling such as had overwhelmed her at Riccardo's touch. She pitied Gigi as she might have pitied a rebellious, unhappy child, and she returned his kiss with tenderness, but no passion.

Somewhere she heard a faint click. Then Gigi pulled away from her abruptly, and she realised that the light in the hall had been switched on.

"Charming," said a soft, mocking voice.

Riccardo stood in the doorway to the living room surveying both of them with a sardonic smile.

"My congratulations, signorina," he said. "Your talent for getting on intimate terms with my family is considerable."

Gigi turned a white, bitter face on him. *"Vai all'inferno!"* Go to hell.

Riccardo gave a short laugh. He too spoke in Italian. "As you are doing? I think not. It is enough that one of us treads that path and brings grief to our mother."

"Do not speak of our mother to me!" shouted Gigi.

"I do not intend to speak to you any further tonight. You are more than a little drunk. I suggest you go quietly to bed." Riccardo switched back to English. "Signorina, if you please, I should like a word with you before you go upstairs."

He turned away into the room without waiting for her response. Karen looked at Gigi to see how he would take this peremptory way of dismissing him. His face was strained, and he seemed on the edge of losing control. Then a wicked grin twisted his features and he sauntered after Riccardo. In the doorway he stopped and waited for

Karen to pass him. Then he leaned forward and kissed her again on the mouth. His eyes were on his brother.

"*Buona notte, cara,*" he said in a clear voice. "And thank you. It was a wonderful night—every moment of it."

He wandered off towards the staircase, leaving her alone with Riccardo.

"I think I'll go up too," she said, furious with both of them. "Good night."

"Signorina." Riccardo's voice was like ice, and it stopped her in her tracks. "Oblige me by remaining. I will not detain you long."

Despite his apparent calm she could sense the anger radiating from him in almost tangible waves. She shrugged and moved away from him towards the fireplace.

The low mosaic table was covered with papers, some of which consisted of columns of figures. Riccardo had been sitting up late to work. Before that he had obviously been out. His dinner jacket lay tossed on a nearby chair, but apart from that he was still dressed. The black trousers might have been designed to emphasise the length of his legs. His dress shirt was casually costly, made of pale blue silk, the front heavily embroidered, tailored to fit exactly over his lean frame. At some point Riccardo had opened the neck so that the brown column of his throat rose austerely from the silk. He could have been a medieval Italian prince, peacocklike in his ability to wear clothes of almost feminine softness and use them to underline his vital masculinity.

And a prince, Karen realised, was what he was—a prince facing a threat to his authority and considering how to deal with it. The Italians were legendary for their subtlety and ruthlessness in dealing with usurpers, and Riccardo had shown himself capable of both. If he could not seize Karen's territory in combat he planned to acquire it by a treaty of marriage.

He regarded her in silence for a long moment before leaving the door and walking towards her. She refused to give him the satisfaction of asking what he wanted. Over the fireplace Alfonso laughed down at the scene he had brought about.

"You are staking your claim, aren't you, Karen?" Riccardo said quietly. "Only two days here and already you make yourself very much at home." His eyes raked her, taking in the low-cut dress, the diamonds. "You look different tonight, harder—more calculating. I don't have to ask why, do I? Do you think you will capture my brother by such means?"

She gave a gasp of genuine indignation.

"I'm not trying to 'capture' your brother," she cried.

"No? Do you deny that you are trying to turn him into your ally against me?"

"I don't need to. You must know that he's already against you."

"And you think you can twist that to your own advantage?"

"If you're incautious enough to leave yourself exposed to that kind of attack, why shouldn't I take advantage of it?" she said spiritedly.

"Because you would be meddling with things you should not dare to touch. My private . . . differences . . . with my brother are not your concern, and for all our sakes I am requesting you not to make use of them."

"Thus robbing me of my most effective weapon and leaving you with a clear field?" she said. "What would I fight you with, Riccardo, if I couldn't win an ally?"

"Must we fight?" he asked in an unexpectedly mild tone. "I thought we agreed last night that you were to take your place on the board and I would cease my objections? I even gave you some material to help you. Material that you should have been studying, instead of staying out with Gigi till this hour."

"If I stayed out till dawn it would be none of your business," she cried. "Keep out of my private life."

"Unfortunately your private life now affects us all. And it is only a few moments ago that I asked you to stay out of *my* private life. You responded with a declaration that all was fair in war. I repeat my question: Why are we fighting? I thought we had agreed to a truce."

She bit her lip. She was not ready to reveal how she knew that the truce he offered was a sham.

"I don't trust you," she said at last. "I just don't believe you'd give up that easily. I'm not lowering my guard until I see your next move."

He gave an eloquent shrug. "Perhaps you are wise. Very well, I accept your challenge. If you are determined to fight, we fight. And we do so on the terms that *you* have just declared—that all is fair in war. If my private life is not off-limits to you, then neither is yours to me."

"What do you mean?"

"You will notice that until this moment I have refrained from speculating about where you and Gigi have been until this hour."

"That's none of your business—"

"It's very much my business if you're up to what I think you are. Gigi made some silly remarks about marriage this afternoon, but they were only jokes, as you should be adult enough to know. And if you have spent tonight in Gigi's apartment, then let me warn you—as one combatant to another—that no woman ever persuaded him into marriage by *that* method."

He had moved slowly nearer to her so that now he was standing close enough to ward off her flying hand before it could strike him across the face. Karen found her wrist imprisoned in a grip of iron.

"You are most unwise to attempt physical violence with me, Karen," he said softly. "I am much stronger than you, and you would regret it."

Without taking his eyes from hers he dropped his hand, forcing her wrist behind her back.

"Let me go at once," she gasped.

He did not answer, but she felt her other wrist seized and treated in the same fashion. Now both her hands were imprisoned, and she was trapped in the circle of his arms. She could feel the warmth of his body through the thin shirt. Her nostrils were filled with the heady masculine scent of him, musky and exciting. She did not dare look up, for she knew his mouth was dangerously close to hers.

"Let me go," she repeated in a tight, furious voice.

His full curved mouth mocked her. "No. I feel safer like this. Who knows how you might attack me if I released you?"

"Do you call this a civilised way of talking business?" she snapped.

"Business is what I talk with men, Karen. With women the subject is something quite different. If I had any doubts about your total unfitness for the power you hold, you have cleared up the matter by your behaviour tonight."

"But the power's still mine, isn't it?" she taunted him. "And it'll go on being mine no matter what your opinion."

His brow darkened. "You have great confidence. Do not indulge yourself in delusions about my brother. You are not going to marry him and use him against me. I shall not permit that."

"You would have no power to prevent it. Gigi doesn't need your permission to marry, and neither do I."

He leaned low to speak softly into her ear, and she felt his breath scorch her skin.

"You are wrong, Karen," he murmured. "I could not prevent Gigi from marrying you, but I could prevent *you* from marrying *him*."

The surge of delight that shook her as his lips touched the tender skin of her neck warned her of his meaning. He knew how easily he could rouse her senses, and this was intended as a casual demonstration of his power. She twisted violently in his embrace and managed to get her wrists free. But even so there was no escape. One hand, pressed into the small of her back, drew her against the hard length of him. The other forced up her chin so that her blazing eyes stared upwards into his black ones. She was aware of their dark glitter for a split second before he dropped his head to press his lips onto hers.

He kissed her in a leisurely manner, his fingers softly caressing the nape of her neck, a spot so sensitive that aching shudders surged through her, and she involuntarily pressed closer to him. She was aware of a thunderous heartbeat, but whether it was his or her own she could not be sure.

She had meant to push him away, but her hands betrayed her. They clung to him and began a sweet exploration of his long, lean frame. Her body had a will of its own. It cared nothing for her mind's distrust of Riccardo. It simply wanted to belong to this man, to lie with him in the joyous exchange of passion, to revel in his caresses, giving back pleasure for pleasure.

He began to tremble beneath her hands, and she knew with a deep instinct that he had been taken by surprise, invaded by a tide of desire which he would beat back if he could because it threatened his control of the situation. For a moment she thought he would thrust her away. His face seemed to hover above hers for an eternity of indecision. Then his black brows contracted and his mouth came down crushingly on hers. She felt, rather than heard, his groan as he yielded reluctantly to his own passion. His kiss was bruising, as though he sought revenge for her power over him.

She could feel his taut body along the length of her own, the powerful thighs pressing hard against hers, communicating their heat through the thin material of her dress.

With every fibre of her being she longed to discard that dress and lie with him naked, burning from the touch of his skin against her own.

As though they were linked by one mind, one desire, Riccardo's hand tore ruthlessly at the thin straps of her dress. She felt the chill on her bare flesh as the material was wrenched down. There was a tearing sound as he ripped his shirt open to the waist so that he could crush her against his naked chest. She felt the hairs rasp against her soft skin in a sensation so erotic that she gasped aloud and ground her fingernails into his back.

She barely knew that his lips were burning the hollow of her neck. All sensations were merged into one all-enveloping flood of desire, as though every nerve end in her body had become alive to him and his longed-for touch. Her fingers clenched convulsively in the thick hair at the back of his head, and she heard him give a deep groan that might have signified pain or fulfilment as his caressing lips slid down the soft curves of her breast and found a nipple.

She felt herself lifted and laid gently on the sofa. Her head swam as his hands began, with deft, expert movements, to remove her remaining clothing. But for a split second her mind cleared, as though a flash of lightning had lit up a darkened landscape. In that blinding moment she saw with terrifying clarity how easily she had discarded her own warnings. She knew Riccardo was playing a cynical game with her, yet she had allowed her passion for him to lure her to the brink of betraying herself. If she did not act now she was lost. Gathering all her strength she thrust him aside with a violent movement.

"*No!*" she exploded. She sat up, shaking her head to clear it, the words tumbling out of her in fear and fury. "Not this way. I won't be taken like some cheap—"

She caught her breath in a sob, and hurled herself up from the sofa. But her senses were still reeling, and she would have fallen if Riccardo's arms had not been there to steady her. He held her in a light, strong embrace, while she clung to him, fighting to subdue her feelings. When he spoke his voice was very quiet, and though it still vibrated with passion she knew he had command of himself.

"You are right," he said. "It must not be like this. When we make love I must know that your whole heart is in it."

"*When* we make love," she echoed angrily. "How confident you are. It will never happen. *Never,* do you hear?"

Then he did the thing that almost destroyed the last of her self-control. He drew her gently towards him and said softly into her ear, "*Mia piccola rosa inglese, tanto bella da infiammare il cuore di un uomo, ma con spine tanto documinate da strapparglieto dal petto se fosse tanto incauto da innamorarsi di te. Ma un giorno . . . un giorno . . .*"

Dazed, she stared at him, unable to believe the words she had heard. He searched her face for a moment, then said, "You do not understand me, *cara.* But soon you will know the meaning of my words—and why I tread a cautious path towards you. Until then . . ."

He was talking to empty air. Karen had wrenched herself out of his grasp and fled the room. She managed to get to her own bedroom without being seen, and threw herself, weeping and laughing together, across her bed. The tears were pouring down her face even as her heart sang, for Riccardo's words had been, "My little English rose—with beauty to inflame a man's senses, yet full of thorns to tear his heart if he were so reckless as to love you. But one day . . . one day . . ."

Her escape had been an act of desperation lest she yield to her feelings there and then, forgetting that the battle between them was far from over. But as she lay there her heart was joyfully echoing his words: *One day . . . one day . . .*

Chapter Five

She drove into Rome with Gigi the following morning, having left her departure to the last possible minute to avoid a meeting with Riccardo. Her mind was in a riot of confusion about him, and she preferred to delay as long as possible the moment when she must look him in the face. Perversely she found herself in a thoroughly ill temper with Gigi.

"Are you angry with me, Karen?" he said when they were on the autostrada.

"I'm furious with you," she said coldly. "And you'd better drop the subject, Gigi. If I said all I had on my mind it would probably disturb your driving."

His answer was to take both hands off the steering wheel, put them behind his head and stare up into the sky.

"Gigi," she shrieked. *"For the love of heaven!"*

In a flash his hands were on the wheel again. Miraculously the car had not swerved. Gigi grinned from ear to ear. His thin face had the look of a satyr.

"I was just trying to show you that my driving is good enough to cope with anything you can say," he told her. "We were in no danger. My word on it."

"I wouldn't take your word on the date if I were holding

a calendar," she snapped, her nerves in shreds. "A child has more sense of responsibility."

"Are you angry with me for now, or last night?" he asked pointedly.

"Both. But chiefly last night. How *dare* you kiss me—"

"You didn't seem to object," he said mildly.

"I don't mean the first time. I mean the second—when Riccardo was there. You did it on purpose, as a gesture. As for what you said—"

"I merely said it had been a delightful evening," he complained.

"You implied a lot more than that. You were deliberately trying to give Riccardo a false idea."

"What's wrong with that? If I made it sound as though we were lovers, it's because I would like to be your lover, *cara*. You can't blame me for a little wishful thinking."

His voice was that of a hurt little boy, but Karen was immune from his charm this morning. She had glimpsed the spite behind it too clearly. And after a sleepless night it was a relief to be able to vent her feelings on him.

For a second night she had lain awake, brooding about Riccardo. At first there had been joyful euphoria at the words he had spoken, words that seemed to suggest that he was fighting a losing battle against the attraction she held for him. But in the wee small hours, as the room became suffused with a dull grey light, she had suddenly seen things in a new and ominous light.

Everything she had thought she had detected in him—the passion, perhaps the beginnings of something more—might all be no more than a move in the skillful game he was playing against her. He was playing for the highest stakes of all—ultimate control of the company. He was even prepared to marry her to get control. How easy he would find a little calculated lovemaking.

Then his voice would speak again in her mind, anguished, passionate, *"Mia piccola rosa inglese . . ."* The whispered words sounded as though they had been wrenched out of him by torture, words that he had not meant her to understand.

But then there was Gigi's voice, too, repeating, "Rik *never* does anything for anybody except himself. When he really seems to be considering your interests, that is when you should look at him most closely and ask what *he* is getting out of it."

And what Riccardo wanted from her was only too obvious, she thought, as the dawn crept in between the curtains and her heart ached. He wanted her vote at the meeting today. And he thought he'd win it in this way. He was wrong.

"Does your silence mean anything?" Gigi's voice broke in on her. "Are you perhaps thinking of giving me my wish and taking me for a lover?"

"You don't really want us to be lovers any more than I do, Gigi," she said. "Except that you want a way of spiting your brother."

"It doesn't hurt to frighten him a little, *cara*. It does him good to know that everything is not going to be his own way. You should consider what I said about that apartment."

"I have," she said abruptly, "and I think you're right. It won't do for me to be living in your family home. Where is this place?"

"In the centre of the city, near Giulietta's home. Very select, very discreet. I've had my apartment about five years. It's a modern block. I was one of the first in. Almost the first. Rik was ahead of me."

"Riccardo has an apartment there?"

"No more. When I moved in, he moved out. It wasn't discreet for us to be having our hideaways so close together, you see. He was furious."

Karen gave him a wry look. If she knew Gigi—and she was beginning to feel that she did—it was not coincidence that he had moved close to Riccardo. His aim had been to embarrass his brother, and he had apparently succeeded.

"What do you mean, *hideaway?*" she said at last. "I thought Riccardo had a villa somewhere?"

"He does. It's up in the hills."

Karen was silent for a moment, then she asked as casually as she could manage, "And what about his wife? Where did she live?"

"At the villa. Riccardo never took her to the apartment. It wasn't a place for wives."

"You mean it was a place for girl friends?" she said tartly.

He sniggered. "Well, Rik was never the most faithful of husbands."

Karen sat in silence, giving herself a lecture. She was glad of what she had been told. Now she was well armoured against Riccardo. Everything that had happened last night had been a cynical maneuvre designed to win her to his side in today's crucial vote. Determinedly she fixed her thoughts on the coming meeting, where she would have her chance at a little *vendetta*. In that, at least, she was learning to behave like an Italian.

The boardroom was on the fourth floor. It had a high, decorated ceiling and plain green walls on which hung several pictures. Two floor-to-ceiling windows took up most of one wall. In the centre was a round, rosewood table, set out with paper and pencils. There were five chairs. To one side was a smaller table bearing cups and a coffee percolator. Riccardo's secretary was fussing there as Karen and Gigi entered.

Riccardo and his mother were already present. He was standing by one of the windows, studying a sheet of typed paper. He gave Karen a brief nod and a faint, impersonal smile, which she returned. Now that the first moment was over she felt she could take her cue from him and behave indifferently.

"If everyone is ready," said Riccardo at last, "I think we may start." When they were all seated he began to speak in Italian.

"Prevedo che non si saranno obiezioni se, finche avremo eletto un nuovo presidente, agiro io come presidente."

"One moment, please." Gigi spoke in English. "I believe this meeting should be conducted in English—"

"That is quite out of the question," Riccardo also spoke in English. His tone was curt.

"I fail to see why," Gigi persisted. "We all speak English, and without it Karen will not be able to understand what is going on."

"That cannot be our concern," said Riccardo. "While it is true that we all speak English, it is not our native language. This is an Italian company, and it would be intolerable if its board meetings were to be conducted in a foreign language. There is also the paperwork. Are you suggesting that the entire business of the company be conducted in English to suit one person?"

"It's Karen's company too, now," said Gigi maliciously. "At least, twenty-five percent of it is. I move that in future twenty-five percent of all meetings and paperwork be conducted in English."

An imp of fun danced in his eyes as he baited his brother. Karen suppressed a little smile. Gigi's humour had a will-o'-the-wisp quality which was either delightful or infuriating, depending on your point of view. A glance at Riccardo's face left her in no doubt which he found it.

"Your motion is out of order since the meeting has not yet begun," he said coldly. "And I must repeat my insistence that the proper language for us to use is Italian. Miss Conway is here at her own insistence, having assured me that she felt completely capable of undertaking her duties. I'm sure she would be the first to agree that it is for her to accommodate herself to the company, and not the other way around."

He looked directly at Karen as he spoke, and his eyes were alight with the challenge he offered. It was as though he had thrown down a glove between them. She met his gaze without flinching and replied sweetly, *"Capisco perfettamente, posso pero rassicurare i presenti che la mia presenza non li obbliga minimamente a cambiare la prassi."*

There was a moment's thunderstruck silence while they all digested what she had said: I understand perfectly, and I can assure everyone here that there is no need for you to alter your normal methods of business on my account.

Then Gigi's loud crack of laughter split the air. He leaned back in his chair and laughed and laughed.

"Brava, cara," he said at last. "How you have made fools of us all."

"I do not understand," said the signora in her languid way. "You speak Italian, Signorina Conway?"

"Yes. I didn't mention it before because everyone took it for granted that I did not, and there never seemed to be the right moment. I didn't want to seem impolite. . . ."

"You need not elaborate, Miss Conway," said Riccardo. "To me, at least, your reasons for keeping silent are perfectly clear."

For the first time since she dropped her bombshell she looked at him and knew a little jolt of surprise. His reaction was not what she had expected. Instead of the thunderous temper she had thought to see in his face there was a cool, appraising look that might almost have been tinged with humour. He was regarding her through narrowed eyelids as though making a quick reassessment of a foe he had underestimated.

There was anger behind that gaze, she realised, but it was directed not at her, but at himself, for falling into the trap of his own making. There was respect, too, and the slow nod he gave her might almost have been a salute acknowledging a round conceded to her.

She found that her opinion of Riccardo had climbed a couple of notches. He might be an arrogant dictator, but he wasn't petty.

He began to speak in Italian again. His tone was brisk and efficient, dismissing what had just passed.

"Now that we have cleared that little matter up, I suggest we proceed." He looked round the table. "I will repeat what I said before—assuming that there are no objections, I shall take the chair at this meeting until we have formally elected a new chairman."

There were no objections. Everyone seemed to be holding his breath.

"Then perhaps we can go straight ahead with the election of a chairman?"

Riccardo managed the business of proposing himself for office simply and with a total lack of embarrassment. He sincerely believed himself the best man for the job, and he explained why, without apparent conceit.

"I know my father's mind in this matter," he concluded. "It was always his intention that I, as his eldest son, should succeed him as chairman of the company. He trained me with that end in mind. I seek to comply with his wishes and to carry on his work in the way he would have wanted."

Karen felt a reluctant admiration. Riccardo, with his quiet dignity, presented an impressive contrast to his brother, and she had no doubt that what he said was the truth. It was a brave and lonely speech.

"I should like to say something," said the signora.

Karen's eyes were on Riccardo at that moment, and so she was in time to catch the look he threw his mother. She drew in her breath at what she saw clearly written on his face. It was over in a split second, and his features were again impassive. Even hope was wiped from them.

"I am a woman," said the signora, speaking slowly and delicately. "I know little of business, even this one that my own husband built up with so much work over so many years. But I too knew my husband's mind, and I knew that also important to him was his family."

The signora outlined her plan. Gigi listened, his head on

one side, his expression that of a cat who has swallowed the cream. Riccardo looked at his hands, resting on the table. Something in the tense set of his head told Karen that he was forcing himself not to look at his mother.

"Enough. I have finished," said the signora at last. "I wish to see both my sons as chairmen, and for this plan I shall vote."

"And I," said Gigi at once.

Riccardo had picked up a pencil and was scribbling something on the pad before him. He did not look at Karen as he said, "Signorina, your vote?"

As if listening to someone else Karen heard her own voice say, "I vote against the plan."

She had the satisfaction of seeing his head shoot up. She heard Gigi gasp and was aware that the signora had stiffened, but she kept her eyes on Riccardo. He was staring back at her as if unsure whether he had heard properly. There was something unnaturally rigid about the lines of his face, as though he had put on a protective mask.

"Perhaps you do not fully understand what you are voting for—" he began.

"I understand perfectly. I vote against the joint chairmanship."

Riccardo's voice was formal. "To whom then do you give your vote?"

"As I understand it, there is only one other candidate—yourself."

"And naturally his vote will go to himself," came Gigi's jeering voice. "Which makes fifty-five per cent against forty-five. We are out-voted, Mama."

Karen would not meet Riccardo's eyes. She had done the thing she had sworn not to do, and still she didn't know why. Until the last minute she had intended to vote against Riccardo, and yet she had not done so.

She was also grappling with the unexpected discovery

that Riccardo had not counted on her vote. His eyes had betrayed him. He had been as amazed at her action as she had herself.

"Perhaps we could have some coffee now, Lisa." His quiet voice broke the spell.

"I need something a good deal stronger than coffee," Gigi snapped. "It was a mistake for me to go to bed when I did last night, wasn't it? You took your chance, eh, Rik? I wish I knew just what went on after I left."

"Your observation is an insult to Signorina Conway," said Riccardo coldly.

But he spoke formally, as though his mind were elsewhere, and Karen saw a sudden tension in his face. He had reacted calmly when she revealed that she spoke Italian because he had seen it only as a business matter. But now, as the memories of last night came flooding back, its true significance dawned on him. She could have laughed aloud as for a moment the suave businessman vanished to be replaced by the eternal male trapped helplessly in the web of a woman's ingenuity.

Their eyes met for a moment. He was giving her a speculative look, his eyebrows raised the merest fraction. But Karen kept her face steady, refusing to answer his silent question.

"Perhaps I'm better informed about the company's needs than you all realise," she said. She tapped the dossier, which lay on the table before her. "This was very kindly prepared for me by someone who was anxious that I should be well informed, and I can promise you that I learned a very great deal from it."

Riccardo's lips twitched in an uncontrollable grin, which transformed him. He met Karen's eyes with a look of appreciation. His face was illuminated with the mischief she had seen once before, when he had given her the dossier yesterday. For a brief moment they were conspirators, sharing a secret joke, and Karen longed suddenly to know more about this other side of him.

She put a sharp halt on her rioting thoughts and gave herself a warning. That way danger lay. It should be no surprise to her that Riccardo could be charming when it suited him. And why shouldn't he be charming now? He'd got what he wanted, and he was probably congratulating himself. Doubtless he now thought that his lovemaking had seduced her over to his side. But in just a minute he was going to discover his mistake. The dossier contained a high explosive, if he only knew it.

Riccardo took them efficiently through the business at hand, starting with a review of the firm's position on its founder's death. Karen gathered that the last ten years had been spent consolidating past gains, but Alfonso had felt that the time had come for fresh expansion.

"The details were left in my hands," said Riccardo, "and I made some tentative moves, which can go no further till the board approves."

"I have tested the opinion of all our senior management, and they unanimously agree that the future lies in the video industry. We must build new factories, especially equipped for this work. Several sites have been under review. The most promising one is in the north, near Milan. You all have the details. . . ."

He waited while Gigi and Karen shuffled their papers. The signora sat impassive.

"I do not think," said Gigi, with the air of one giving the matter great deliberation, "that my father was of the opinion that the Milan site was the most promising. It has the disadvantage of being the most expensive. Milan is already a great centre for industry and, consequently, land round there is at a premium. If we were to buy somewhere in the South we would have all the benefits of cheaper land, plus a government grant to encourage us. And the labour is cheaper down there."

"It is also less efficient," said Riccardo bluntly. "I know all the arguments for building in the South. Put up your factory in Calabria and the government will practically pay you to do it. And why? Because no one in their right mind will go there and employ semiliterate peasants who can't be persuaded to clock in on time."

His tone was dismissive, implying that the last word in the argument had been said. And the worst of it, Karen realised, was that he was probably right in everything he said. How did you deal with a man whose supreme self-confidence was based on the fact that he really did know better than those around him? Well, it was worth the attempt.

"I notice," she said, "that this site has been under review for some time now."

"That is correct," said Riccardo formally.

"Almost four months. If the site is as valuable as the information here suggests—" she indicated the report that she had taken from the dossier "—I'm surprised that a decision hasn't been made before this."

"There is a great deal of money involved, signorina, as I'm sure you must realise. That kind of investment cannot be made without the fullest investigations beforehand. There have had to be lengthy discussions—"

Gigi interrupted him with a loud guffaw. "Lengthy discussions. I like that! Don't be deceived, Karen. That's just Riccardo's way of saying that he and Papa have been at it hammer and tongs since this was first proposed. Papa was all for a southern site, but Riccardo was determined to do things his own way. And there's nothing to stop him now, is there? I suppose we can assume you'll support him."

"Don't be so certain of that," Karen told him. "There are still some things I'm not satisfied about. To begin with, I should like to know how we can be sure this land is still available to us after so long."

"I can assure you that it is," said Riccardo.

"May the board know how you can be so certain?" enquired Karen sweetly.

"Because I have taken action to ensure that it is."

"May the board know the precise nature of that action?" Karen persisted, still in the same honeyed tone.

He threw her a grim look. "Because I have taken an option on that land which still has a month to run," he declared.

Gigi sat up straight, his eyes glinting. "Did Papa know about this?" he demanded.

"Eventually, yes. At the time I took out the option he was abroad, and I was fully empowered to act in his absence. I informed him when he returned."

"May we know the size of the option?" said Karen.

"Four thousand million lire," said Riccardo calmly.

Karen gasped. That was roughly two million pounds, and he spoke as though discussing the price of cheese.

"It will, of course, be discounted against the final purchase price," Riccardo added.

"If we decide to buy," Gigi reminded him. "If we don't, the money's lost."

"There is no reason for it to be lost," said Riccardo angrily. "This is simply the most suitable site."

"What a pity that you never apparently managed to convince Papa of that," said Gigi dryly.

"That's the bit I don't understand," Karen agreed. "With so much money committed already, why didn't Alfonso just give in?"

"I'll tell you why," said Gigi. "You may have noticed, Karen, that my brother has a habit of simply arranging things the way he thinks they ought to be and telling people afterwards. For this he was constantly at odds with my father, who did exactly the same himself. Papa liked to make all the decisions, and when Riccardo tried to present him with a *fait accompli,* he got very angry. In the end, though, he always gave in. Except this time. Riccardo had gone too far."

Riccardo was white-faced, but he retained his composure.

"You have a taste for the melodramatic, Gigi," he said

coldly. "Truly our father was mistaken not to let you become an opera singer."

"Can we come back to the point?" said Karen. "Why did Alfonso hold out?"

"Because he was an old man," said Riccardo, "and like many old men he had become sentimental about the region of his birth. Only a madman would have tried to build a factory in Calabria, but he wouldn't see it. He allowed his feelings to cloud his judgement."

"Well, anyone's judgement can be at fault," said Karen mildly. "Haven't you ever made a mistake?"

"We all make mistakes," he said, exasperated. "But I do not believe I have made a major error in such a matter as this."

"Aren't you forgetting Innoccino?" she said.

There was a silence, as though time had stopped. Karen kept her eyes on Riccardo and knew that her moment of *vendetta* had come. That old, old mistake—a young man's error—to have that dragged into the light of day ten years later when he had thought it was all buried and forgotten. How that must gall his proud spirit.

"I don't understand," said Gigi. "What is this?"

"I daresay you wouldn't know about it," said Karen. "You'd have been about seventeen at the time. Innoccino is a small town about eighty miles south of here. Ten years ago Tornese acquired a tract of land there for the purpose of building factories. It was excellent land for this, extensive and unused since the war. Also the price was incredibly—one might almost say suspiciously—cheap."

She stopped. It was ridiculous, of course, but the black fury in Riccardo's eyes was making her heart thump erratically.

"Continue," he said through gritted teeth. "Do not, I pray you, miss one single detail. Let us all enjoy the story."

"It isn't a long story," said Karen. "After the transaction was completed, and the money had changed hands—only then was it discovered that the land had been designated for agricultural purposes, and nothing could be built on it. Tornese owned a large tract of useless land."

Gigi rocked with silent laughter, and even the signora allowed herself to smile. Riccardo had command of himself, but Karen guessed he was fighting to suppress his temper. She had committed the unforgiveable crime of exposing him to ridicule, and she had revealed him as fallible.

"But what is the end of the story?" begged Gigi when he had calmed down. "Now I remember Innoccino. We have factories there. How did they come to be built?"

"Permission was eventually granted," said Karen. "But it took a great deal of . . . negotiation."

"You mean that my father had to bribe every official for a hundred miles," said Riccardo softly. "It cost him a fortune, and he threw it up at me regularly till the day he died. Now I discover that he also discussed it with you."

There was a quiet bitterness in his voice that gave her a little shock. And suddenly she knew that she had done more than damage Riccardo's pride. She had dealt him a savage blow where it would hurt him most. Alfonso must have cast a gigantic shadow over his children, but mostly over his eldest son, who wanted to emulate his father's achievements and win that father's esteem. The memory of this early failure still had the power to wound him, but what seared him most of all was Alfonso's derision, and the thought that he had shared his laughter with others.

She found that the revenge which had been so sweet only a moment ago had turned to ashes in her mouth. She felt like a jouster who had tilted a lance in friendly combat in the lists, and had accidentally dealt his rival a mortal blow.

It wasn't pleasant to feel ashamed of herself, but she couldn't escape the sensation. What she had done now seemed trivial and silly. She tried to remind herself of her own real grievances against Riccardo, but she was only aware of an overwhelming desire to comfort him.

"May I ask, *signorina,* what is the point of these reminiscences?" said Riccardo.

"I was . . . merely trying to suggest that nobody is infallible," she managed to say.

"Perhaps you were implying that I am no more skilled in these matters than I was as a young man of twenty-five, negotiating his first deal?"

"Of course I'm not suggesting that. But you do seem to have handled this almost entirely alone, and since it is evident that a very large amount of money is going to be involved—"

"You would like to hold my hand and make sure I spend it wisely, so that your inheritance is not squandered."

"That's a shocking thing to say," she snapped, angered by his ironic tone. "But I do think this business needs more investigation—"

"In short you would like to see the land for yourself and talk to all the officials to make sure I haven't slipped up again?"

"I don't see why I shouldn't."

"Very well. In that case let us waste no more time." Riccardo stood up. "The meeting is adjourned. It will be rescheduled at some later date when the signorina has satisfied herself that all is in order."

His abruptness took everyone by surprise. He was putting his papers together as he spoke, and the others started to do the same. Karen was conscious of a feeling of dismay. Riccardo had nettled her until her momentary pity for him had vanished, and now her temper had betrayed her into saying something she didn't mean. What was worse, she was committed to action without having any idea how to go about it.

"Are you ready, Karen?" said Riccardo briskly.

"Ready for what?"

"To go to Milan. I thought that was where you wanted to go."

"Yes, but—"

"Then hurry, please." He took her arm and began to shepherd her out of the room. At the door he turned. "Mama, I hope you will forgive this abrupt departure. We may be away for a couple of days. It depends on how long it takes Karen to get through everything she has to do."

Karen was whisked out of the door before she could add anything to this. She found herself perforce going with Riccardo to the lift. His grip on her arm was gentle enough, but she had learned already how deceptive that gentleness could be, and she wasn't going to risk struggling with him in a public corridor. Not until the lift doors closed behind them and they were on their way down did she speak to him.

"What on earth do you mean, hauling me off like that?" she demanded. "I don't want to go to Milan."

"You informed me that you did," he said, his face a mask of innocence.

"Yes, but not like this. Not today."

"There is no time to lose. That option runs out in a month."

"I don't care. I'm not going to be ordered about in this manner."

"There is no way you can prevent it. I warned you that if you interfered, you might find the results unexpected. You made your own choice. This lift will stop in a moment. I advise you not to attempt flight."

The doors opened, and he grasped her arm again. She could feel his fingers on her bare flesh. They were warm and strong, and tensed—ready to hold her if she tried to escape.

Then a thought occurred to her, and she gave a mental shrug. There was no point in making an issue of it here. It would be easier to wait until they had returned home to pack. Once there she could lock her door against Riccardo and there would be nothing he could do.

She sat demurely beside him as the car weaved its way out of the city traffic. He seemed to have forgotten her presence. Karen leaned back and closed her yes. After a while she opened them again, and realised that none of the scenery was familiar.

"Where are we going?" she demanded.

"To the airport. Not Leonardo da Vinci, but the other one. Rome has a second, smaller airport, used for charter flights and private planes."

"But aren't we going to the villa first?"

"No. Why should we?"

"To pack. If we're going to be away overnight we can't just leave like this."

"I have a permanent hotel suite in Milan, with some clothes already there."

"But I haven't."

"You can buy whatever you need when we get there. If you are short of money, the firm's credit is good anywhere."

She gaped at the high-handedness of it. Her mind refused to take in the cool way he had outwitted her.

"*Take me back!*" she exploded at last. "I won't be . . . *abducted* like this."

"I'm afraid you have no choice."

She could have sworn he was grinning, although he kept his face to the front and she could see only part of his expression.

"You think you've covered everything, don't you?" she fumed.

"I usually manage to account for all the details. My negligence of ten years ago has never been repeated."

"And suppose when we get to the airport we can't get on a flight?"

"There is no question of that. My private plane will be

waiting for us. By now Lisa will have called the airport and my plane will be standing on the tarmac with its engines running."

She tried to keep her temper at boiling point, but it was no good. The situation was too ridiculous. She leaned back in her seat and began to laugh. He gave her a quick sideways glance, and the grin spread over his face.

"You're a good loser," he said approvingly.

"Don't be deceived, Riccardo. I haven't lost yet," she assured him.

But she was smiling as she spoke. She had discovered that she wasn't really averse to a trip alone with him after all.

Chapter Six

As Riccardo had predicted, they found the light aircraft waiting on the tarmac, its engines warming. He drove right up to it. Someone opened the car door on Karen's side. Someone else got in and drove it away. Riccardo never gave a backward look. He seemed to take it for granted that things would be where he wanted them, and removed when he wanted them removed.

Karen boarded the plane and found the interior luxuriously furnished. The large seats might have been armchairs, except that they had safety belts. There was a liquor cabinet and a small kitchen, complete with steward. Karen tried to remember not to gape, but this was her first taste of real, high-powered luxury, and it was hard to behave as though she lived like this every day. Just as she was about to seat herself Riccardo said, "I thought you'd prefer to be up here."

He led the way to the front and pulled back a curtain over a door. Karen moved through and found herself in the pilot's cabin.

"You sit there," said Riccardo, indicating a seat next to the pilot.

Bemused, she obeyed him. "I should have thought you'd want to sit here," she said.

"No, I sit *here.*" Riccardo dropped down into the pilot's seat and began to strap himself in. "Fasten your belt," he commanded.

"You mean, you're going to fly this thing?"

"Of course. Why not? I have an international pilot's license. There is also an official pilot, but I've left him in the back."

At once they heard the outer door of the aircraft slamming shut. There was a small bustle outside, on the ground. The engines, which had been humming, buzzed into louder life, and the plane began to drift forward. Riccardo had donned a set of headphones through which he was apparently receiving instructions from the control tower. From time to time he answered into a microphone resting on his chest.

When they reached the start of the runway the engine-note rose higher till it was almost a scream, the little aircraft zoomed forward, the bumpy movement became suddenly smooth, and they were airborne.

Karen was exhilarated. She was flying above the clouds, alone in a private world with Riccardo. At the back were the steward and the pilot, but she could ignore them. There were only herself and Riccardo in this tiny cabin, surrounded by sky.

She studied him, but he seemed completely unaware of her. All his attention was given to controlling the plane. His eyes were fixed on three rows of dials in front of him. They made Karen's eyes cross, but Riccardo seemed to make perfect sense of them. She looked at his hands, so strong and sure in what they were doing, with never a second's hesitation. There was the tang of excitement in the thought that her life was in those hands, that only Riccardo's skill was keeping her safe, thousands of feet up. She felt again that sense of perfect confidence she had known the first night, driving beside him in the car. This was a man who made her feel that he could be master of anything he chose.

Except me, she thought. After this morning he knows I can fight him on his own ground, and beat him. And I will. But he's still got most of the cards. Which one will he play against me next, I wonder? Whatever it is, I'm ready for it.

She could have laughed aloud with the sudden, intoxicating sense of being alive as never before. Life—and love—are nothing without a challenge. They were his own words, and her heart echoed them joyfully. She had met a man who challenged her as no other man had ever done, as poor David Brightwell would not have dared to do. And she loved him. It was pointless to pretend any longer that the overwhelming attraction he had for her was merely the sexual pull of his male magnetism. It was far, far more. She loved him because he dared her, duped her—but then fell into her traps in a way that caught at her heart.

But why now, she wondered? Why had the understanding come this minute? Surely not because she'd been, literally, swept off her feet. She let her mind wander back over the morning until it reached the significant moment.

It was when the signora had started to speak, and Riccardo had looked at his mother, knowing what she was going to say. Karen had seen that look, had read its depths of almost incredulous pain, and known that Giulietta was right when she had said that Riccardo was jealous of his mother's love for Gigi. It was hard to believe it of the strong, competent man sitting beside her, holding life and death so lightly in his slim brown hands. But he was vulnerable where you would least expect it. He could be deeply hurt in ways he would hate the world to suspect.

Karen had looked at everyone in that boardroom and seen them as though they were under a spotlight. She had seen Gigi acting out of pure spite, and his mother acting out of foolish partiality. It was like watching a lion being baited by jackals, and at the last moment Karen had known that she could not join the jackals.

She could see now that the moment she had rushed to his defence had also been the moment when she started to love him. And later, when she had dragged up that old memory to taunt him, she had been shattered to discover that she felt his pain as her own. But as her first exhilaration began to die down she reflected that she'd been caught between the two jaws of a trap. She'd known that she desired Riccardo, now she knew she loved him. But his feelings were a mystery to her. She had clues, but they pointed in opposite directions.

The journey took just over an hour. When they were near the end Riccardo said, "Look below."

She did so, and saw a turreted castle. It looked several hundred years old, but was in a good state of preservation.

"That's the Lupone Museum," said Riccardo. "It used to be the fortress of the Lupone Dukes. At one time they ruled most of this region. The name has died out now. Only one minor branch of the family survived through the female line, but it is from that my mother comes."

"Oh I remember now—Gigi said something about your mother coming from an old family who'd come down in the world."

"That, of course, depends on your point of view. My mother's family were not poor. Her father owned a small factory making electrical components, and since she was the only child, it eventually became her inheritance. By that time she was married to my father and so it passed to him and became the foundation of his own fortune. But the Lupone dukes, from whom my mother is descended, would certainly have considered a small factory a very trifling matter. And her marriage to a Calabrese peasant—even one on the way up—would have made them turn in their graves."

He began the descent. Karen peered out of the window

until a soft bump announced that they had touched down. Within five minutes of landing they had left the airport.

"We'll be in Milan in half an hour," he said. "We'll check into the hotel first. It has its own shops, so you can get whatever you need while I make some phone calls."

She had loved Rome on sight. With Milan she was instantly indifferent. In Rome history was always present in its statues and ancient buildings. You could, if you were fanciful, believe that Julius Caesar or the Emperor Nero had just slipped round the corner and might slip back again at any moment. But Milan was very much of the present. Its wealth was founded on modern industry and technology. It was glossy, sophisticated and flashily smart.

It didn't surprise Karen that the receptionist at the Hotel Risorgimento was expecting them. She had learned to anticipate that Riccardo's efficient secretary would have telephoned ahead. She was shown to a suite immediately next to Riccardo's. It was palatial, with its own sitting room as well as bedroom and bathroom. For once there was no marble, and the floor was carpeted in pale green. As at the villa, the bed was enormous, a real Italian 'matrimonial bed,' at least six feet wide. Karen remembered Alfonso once saying that an Italian hotel always provided a *letto matrimoniale,* it being the way of Italians to assume that people mated. In no other country of the world was the union of a man and a woman so glorified as here.

Shopping in the hotel's arcade was easy. She had only to sign to have her purchases put on her bill. With this system, extravagance soon became inevitable. She embarked on an orgy of spending such as she had never enjoyed before. She wandered from one boutique to another, enjoying the feeling that she could plunder this Aladdin's Cave with a clear conscience, since Riccardo had snatched her away with only what she stood up in.

She bought makeup and filmy underwear, and a night-dress so sheer it almost vanished at the touch. She didn't actually need new shoes and handbag, but she bought them anyway, so entrancing was the Gucci boutique. She hesitated the longest over the trousers of soft beige suede, sleek and supple, but she bought them in the end because she knew she had the long legs to show them off. Then it seemed a crime not to add the matching jacket and a yellow silk shirt to complete the ensemble.

She began to add up what she'd spent. Halfway through she stopped because she was scaring herself witless. She began to think that Gigi's philosophy of letting the bill come as a surprise might have something to be said for it after all.

Back in her room she showered and dressed in the suede trousers and yellow shirt. She was brushing her hair when there came a knock at the door. She answered and found a pageboy with a trolley on wheels. On the top shelf stood a large ice bucket from which protruded a bottle of champagne.

"For you, signorina," he said.

Bemused, she stood back and allowed him to enter. As he passed she noticed that two glasses stood on the tray. When he reached the centre of the sitting room the boy stopped and said,

"My instructions are not to open the bottle signorina, but to give you this."

He handed her a sealed envelope and stood waiting. She tore it open and read: *I am gambling that you cannot open champagne unaided. If you wish me to do it for you, you must agree to a truce. R.*

Chuckling, Karen seated herself and hurriedly wrote on a sheet of hotel notepaper: *I opened my first champagne bottle at eighteen months—with my teeth. But I should like a truce. K.*

She gave the note to the pageboy and waited. When the door had closed behind him, she glanced quickly at herself in the mirror and noticed how her cheeks had flushed. Her heart, too, had begun to thump erratically. She tried to tell herself that she was being foolish, but it felt as though this was her first real meeting with Riccardo.

She was so lost in these thoughts that she jumped slightly when she heard his knock. He too had changed his clothes from the formal suit of the morning to slacks and an open-necked shirt. His smile was wry, almost tentative, and he waited till she had gestured for him to enter.

"You are sure you have no burning oil perched on top of the door?" he said.

"That went out of fashion with your Lupone ancestors," she said, laughing.

He came in and closed the door behind him. "My Lupone ancestors never indulged in such practises," he said. "That was for barbarians—like the English. The Italian weapon is poison—the subtle murderer that kills from within."

As he spoke he started to open the bottle. The liquid foamed over into the two glasses, and they took one each.

"Truce?" he said.

"Truce."

They clinked glasses and drank.

"But I'd still like to know why," said Karen. "Two hours ago you'd have cheerfully murdered me."

"That is true. But since then I have had time to think, and it has occurred to me that I have far more cause to be grateful to you than to murder you. And I *am* grateful Karen, sincerely grateful."

"For my vote, you mean?"

"Yes. It was the last thing I was expecting to happen."

"Is that really true?" she said lightly. "After last night, didn't you think that you'd seduced me over to your side and had me safely in your pocket?"

He reddened slightly. "I am not quite the lout you appear to believe, Karen. Although perhaps I have only myself to blame for your poor opinion. My recollection of last night is that it ended with you wrenching yourself out of my arms and fleeing from me in bitterness and anger. I would have had to be a monster of conceit to think I 'had you in my pocket' after that."

She drained her glass, turning her head slightly so that he could not see her face. Bitterness and anger, so that was what he thought. Let him go on thinking it. Better that than that he should suspect the truth.

"I should apologise to you for my behaviour last night," he went on. "My only excuse was the lateness of the hour. You realised, I dare say, that I had had too much to drink, and did . . . and said . . . things that normally . . ."

"Yes, that's all right," she interrupted him hastily. She felt a twinge of disappointment. It had not seemed to her that Riccardo had been drinking the previous evening.

"I was angry this morning," he went on. "You made a fool of me about your Italian, but I suppose that was my fault for taking things for granted. And I was even angrier about your dragging up that old business of Innoccino. But after all, they're pinpricks. What really matters is that—for some mysterious reason of your own—you made me chairman. It's been my dream to run my father's firm ever since I was old enough to understand about it. From today I shall, thanks to you. How petty I would be to hate you after that."

"Did you hate me?"

He gave a rueful smile. "No, Karen, I can't hate you. I can want to box your ears, but I can't hate you. I can see that life for us is going to be very lively. There will be many fights, but no hatred."

"I want to tell you something," she said impulsively. "You were wrong about your father discussing Innoccino with me. I only ever heard it mentioned once, and that was ten years ago, just after it happened. He wasn't laughing, either. He was raging up and down, you know the way he used to—"

"Yes, I know." He grinned, and for a moment their eyes met in a moment of shared laughter. Karen felt her heart jolt.

"He was in such a temper that he told my mother," she went on. "But that was all. He had his explosion and it was over. After that the subject was closed forever."

"You could only have been a child ten years ago."

"I was fifteen, and I had big ears. I listened to all sorts of conversations that weren't meant for me."

"But this morning you were so well versed in the details . . . ?"

"That had nothing to do with Alfonso," she said quickly. "I rang a journalist friend of mine in England and got him to look up the file of press cuttings. I'm only telling you this because I want you to know that your father didn't laugh at you behind your back."

There was a silence while he studied his glass.

"Thank you, Karen," he said at last in a quiet voice. "It was kind of you to tell me about this. I was . . . under a false impression, shall we say? Now I know the truth, and I am glad. Let us forget the matter."

He lifted his glass to her again and they saluted. She tried to read his eyes, but they were veiled.

"We'd better start," he said, draining his glass. "We have to drive thirty kilometres to this site. I suggest we stop for lunch on the way."

It took them twenty minutes to get out of the city's traffic jams.

"How do you like Milan?" he asked as they were brought to a halt yet again.

"I don't—the little I've seen of it. Most of the buildings seem to be banks. It's a soulless place."

"Oh, it has a soul. Its soul is money. It's the heart of finance and industry in this country."

"Then why doesn't Tornese have its headquarters here instead of in Rome?"

"Because," said Riccardo simply, "my mother would not hear of it."

"Your mother?" she said, bewildered. "But surely it was a business decision?"

"It was, and it wasn't. It was also a question of where they were to have their home. My mother wanted to live in Rome. It was a dream of hers. My father always said that decisions about the home were for the woman to make."

"Even though it meant situating a multi-million pound empire miles away from the most convenient place?"

"That's right. My mother's home was her empire, and my father respected her rights in the matter."

She laughed. "You enjoyed telling me that, didn't you?"

"I must admit that I did. I would like to remove your image of my mother—or Italian women generally—as down-trodden and subservient. Within their homes they are queens. And perhaps my father's action will persuade you that those are not mere empty words."

She was more impressed than she cared to admit. But it wouldn't do to let him know it.

"Will you want to move everything now?" she said.

"I think not. It would distress my mother, and my father would not have wished it. Besides—" he frowned for a moment "—I too do not wish to leave Rome."

She waited to see if he would go on, but the traffic eased suddenly, and he drove on. A few moments later they were free of the jam and speeding out of Milan. Riccardo seemed to have forgotten their conversation and made no further mention of whatever—or whoever—kept him in Rome.

In the country they drove along rough roads laid between fields of olive trees. Halfway there they stopped at a wayside *trattoria* and sat outside at a rough wooden table for a late lunch. It was spaghetti washed down with a rough red wine that was made locally. To Karen it tasted like the food of the gods.

They were served by the *padrona*, a young woman of about Karen's age with a pregnancy that was just becoming obvious. She had a face that beamed like the sun and she walked with a proud firm step. Once a man who was obviously her husband came out with more wine. As they passed he stopped and laid his hand gently on her stomach. Their eyes met, and they smiled.

Karen found herself also smiling irresistibly, and turned to say something to Riccardo. But she stopped dead at what she saw in his face. He was not looking at her. He might have been looking at the young couple, but it seemed to Karen as though he stared past them into some distance that only he could see. His eyes were bleak and anguished, and something in them made Karen shiver. The disturbing sensation lasted only a moment. Then she heard Riccardo's voice, reassuringly normal, speaking of the land they were going to see.

When they got there it turned out to be a vast stretch of dusty ground. One or two shabby-looking buildings disfigured it. A small shed had been erected nearby, and a man quickly emerged from this. He was middle-aged and well-dressed.

"This is Guido Vitalli, the present owner," said Riccardo. "I called and asked him to be here with all the paperwork ready for your inspection."

"That was very kind of you," said Karen with grim humour. But she was pleased to see that Riccardo was himself again and was even regarding her with an imp of mischief in his black eyes.

Guido bustled over, full of enthusiasm—how glad he was that they had come, so many other prospective purchasers just waiting to jump in the moment the option lapsed—a decision soon, yes?

Riccardo steered them both back into the shed, which turned out to be a makeshift office. He introduced Karen to Guido, who fell all over her. He plainly assumed that she was the one who had been delaying the sale, and he set himself to the task of convincing her to approve it. He produced figures, reports both printed and typed; he showed her letters from government ministers, letters from banks, letters from local officials concerning the laying on of water, gas, electricity, special transport; he stressed how near they were to the airport, the autostrada. Karen listened without taking in a word. All she knew was that Riccardo was watching her with an expression of unholy delight.

After two hours he took pity on her and extricated her from Guido's clutches.

"I think you've seen and heard enough to enable you to form an opinion, have you not signorina?" he asked.

"Thank you, it's been most illuminating," she lied.

"A decision within a few days, Guido," Riccardo promised as he led Karen to the car.He deftly declined Guido's insistent invitation that they honour his house for a meal and put his foot down on the accelerator.

"It would have served you right if I'd accepted for both of us," he told Karen as they made their escape. "You could have listened to him all evening."

"No," she begged, laughing. "Be satisfied with your revenge. I shouldn't have interfered. I should have known you'd have everything under control."

"I see you are a woman of generosity. To reward you I shall buy you the best meal in Milan tonight. After all, I have something to celebrate."

"That sounds lovely," she said enthusiastically. "But do we have to get back yet? Surely we must be in the area of the Lupone Museum?"

"And you would like to see it?" He sounded pleased. "It's getting late, but we may get there before it closes."

He drove fast and arrived with half an hour to spare. The castle was already emptying.

"That is good," said Riccardo. "I dislike it when it's crowded with tourists. The more empty it is the better you will get to know my ancestors."

Over the main gateway was a carved stone figure. It had lost some of its sharp outline, but Karen could still make out what it was meant to be.

"It looks like a wolf," she said.

"Of course. Lupone comes from *lupo*, wolf. They were a savage race."

Their feet echoed on the flagstones as they crossed the courtyard. The sun was beginning to set, throwing a deep red glow over the turrets.

"It's magic," Karen breathed.

The atmosphere wrapped them round as soon as they entered. The thick stone walls of the twelfth-century castle shut out the heat of the day. Karen shivered and felt Riccardo's arm go round her, warm and strong.

"I'll fetch your jacket from the car," he said solicitously.

While he was gone she went to the bookstall and bought the guidebook. A quick glance through gave her a rough outline of the history of the Lupone dukes, from their first appearance as warrior lords in the twelfth century to their virtual disappearance in the sixteenth.

The last of the line, said the book, *was the notorious Lodovico. He was an intellectual of enormous culture and learning. But he was also noted for his cruelty. A favourite trick of his was to invite his enemy to dine and offer him a plate of food and a glass of wine—one of which was poisoned. He would then ask the man whether he would prefer to eat or drink. Not knowing where the poison was, the wretched victim would be forced to make a choice. If he chose the poisoned item Lodovico would sit and watch his death agonies. If he chose safely he would be allowed to escape—for the time being.*

Lodovico married three times, each time to his own advantage. His first wife died in childbirth, his second by poison, and the third, a wealthy heiress called Giovanna D'Asselli, managed to survive her husband. Lodovico was assassinated in 1576. He left three daughters and no sons.

"I see you have met my notorious ancestor," said Riccardo, returning with her jacket, which he slipped round her shoulders.

"I'm surprised you own up to him," said Karen. "He seems to have been some kind of monster."

"I do not defend him. But his subjects would have done. Standards were different in those days. As long as he did not increase their taxes, they cared nothing that he poisoned his second wife so that he could marry a third."

"I wondered about that. The book leaves it a bit vague."

His eyes were suddenly full of a teasing humour that made her heart stop. His grin seemed to draw her into a delicious conspiracy.

"And if it's any consolation to your feminist heart," he said, "there is evidence that his third wife was an accomplice in his murder."

"Thank you," she laughed. "I feel a lot better now."

The castle, so grim outside, proved to be a treasure trove within. The great hall struck Karen dumb with wonder. It was over a hundred feet long with an ornate gold-painted ceiling and walls lined with pictures. At the far end was a dais on which stood an elaborate chair. Over the whole arrangement hung a canopy. It was much faded, but Karen could still make out a snarling wolf that had been embroidered there. Looking more closely, she managed to read the words beneath.

"In the mouth of the wolf," she said, wondering.

"It was the Lupone motto. The old dukes were so much feared that it was said anyone who came to this castle came into the mouth of the wolf. They liked that, so they adopted it."

The next room was a small antechamber containing several large glass cases. Most of them held books and letters, but the last one was filled with coins.

"The Lupones were great bankers, too," Riccardo told her. "They put out vast loans to everyone and called them in when it suited them. That gave them total power."

"Total power," she murmured. "How you must envy them."

He grinned. "Total power may be what I want, but something tells me I will never get it while you are around. You have turned out to be a much more formidable opponent than I had anticipated." His tone was cordial, and he slipped his arm round her shoulders to lead her out of the antechamber.

"What a pity for you that you were born in the twentieth century and not the sixteenth," she teased him. "You'd have found it so much easier to eliminate the opposition."

"There was a moment this morning—when you gave me your vote—when I wondered if you had ceased to oppose me."

"Yes, I know. Your face was very interesting just then."

"So you produced Innoccino out of the hat to remind me not to take you for granted. And of course you would never have thought of Innoccino if I had not alerted you to the Milanese land project by giving you that dossier. So I am hoist with my own petard. Tell me, Karen, are you sure there is no Italian blood in you? I do not mean my father. But many centuries ago, did the blood of Machiavelli not pass into your family? You intrigue with as much skill as an Italian. I can pay you no greater compliment."

"Think you can eliminate me?" She laughed.

"I have not the slightest desire to eliminate you. How dull my life would be without you exploding firecrackers at me when I least expect it. And I have a conviction that if I were so unwise as to employ Lodovico's methods on you, you would employ Giovanna's on me."

"Giovanna was the third wife—the one who helped murder him?"

"That is correct. Except that I see you performing the deed alone. I cannot imagine what assistance you could possibly need to obliterate one man."

Laughing, they passed down the long stone corridor to the portrait gallery where hung the likenesses of the Lupone dukes. Karen walked slowly down the line of pictures. It was the last one that held her attention. It showed a man in his thirties with a thin face framed by long black hair. The eyes had a hard steely glitter, contrasting strangely with the curved, sensual mouth. And somewhere in that face was a disconcerting hint of humour. Karen stood and stared at it for a long time. She didn't need to read the plaque underneath to tell her that she was looking at Lodovico—the last in a line of powerful rulers, men who had been the forebears of the one who stood by her side, his handsome black head at an angle, his sensual lips twisted into a wry smile as he watched the realisation dawn on her face.

"It is . . . rather like you," she said uncertainly.

"It is a little. The likeness is not exact, and not everyone sees it. But I thought you would, since in your mind I believe it's a moot point which is the worse monster—my ancestor or myself."

She joined in his laughter.

"Well, I must admit, I've been half-expecting Lodovico to look like you ever since I heard how he disposed of his enemies," she said. "But it's incredible how that face has come down the centuries."

A nearby attendant coughed to indicate that it was time for them to depart. Everyone else had gone, and they were the last left in the echoing gallery. As the man moved close enough to see Riccardo's face clearly he gave a visible start.

"He's seen it too." Riccardo grinned. "If you want to stay, just say so. If he gives us any trouble I'll offer him a choice of food or wine—suitably prepared."

"Speaking of food and wine—you promised me the best meal in Milan," she reminded him.

"And you still want to eat it? Brave girl. Let's go, *cara.*"

Chapter Seven

They did not drive straight to the restaurant but returned to the hotel and separated to prepare for the evening. Karen's first action was to call a boutique she had visited that afternoon and ask them to send up a white jersey dress she had tried on.

The dress had bare arms and a softly draped neck; it moulded itself lingeringly to her curves, then flared slightly so that it clung as she walked. It was knee-length, showing off her long slim calves and ankles. She felt that she looked lovely in it.

Her hair gleamed red and gold, setting off the peachlike perfection of her skin. Strange that she had ever thought blue a cold colour for her eyes. There was nothing cold about them now. They smiled at her from the mirror, rich and brilliant, like a deep blue lake under a summer sky. They were the eyes of a woman who had suddenly discovered love, who was ready to open her arms to the beloved man, if only . . .

Her heart sank a little and some of the glow went out of her. If only she had not overheard Riccardo's conversation with his mother. For it cast a shadow over everything. There was not just the mystery of Alicia. There was also the knowledge that Riccardo had considered marrying her in cold blood. She must never allow herself to forget that his altered manner could be merely another move in their private war. There might be no more behind it than the wish to throw her off-guard.

But some part of her heart could not bring herself to believe that this was true. There was still the memory of Riccardo holding her in his arms, shaking with passion, and whispering in a voice throbbing with suppressed desire, "*Mia piccola rosa inglese. . . .*"

Why had he spoken words of passion in a language he thought she couldn't understand? And today, when he knew the truth, he had tried to wipe those words out, to make her believe he had been too drunk to know what he was saying. Was it because he feared her power to stir his senses, and perhaps his heart? They had laughed together this afternoon, but behind his banter she had sensed the truth of his statement that he had learned to be more wary of her. If she could lure him out from that wariness, perhaps she could learn the truth about his feelings.

At eight o'clock Riccardo knocked at her door. She saw at once that the sight of her had taken him aback. He came inside, kicked the door shut behind him, and stood holding both her hands in his, while his eyes told her she was beautiful. He spoke with self-conscious lightness, as though trying to cover some deeper feeling.

"Why, Karen, you are transformed. How did you manage it in so short a time?"

"I'll never know." She smiled. "Mostly I just bought the first thing I saw. Thanks to you I had to get everything from scratch."

"Everything?" his eyes gleamed wickedly.

"All I had was what I stood up in, you wretch."

He dropped her hands and moved towards the ice bucket where the remains of the champagne still stood. He filled the two glasses and handed her one.

"Let us finish this before we go," he said.

She drained hers quickly and dropped onto a sofa by the window. An afternoon spent mostly in the hot sun had caught up with her suddenly and made her sleepy. She yawned and stretched luxuriously.

"You do that like a cat." Riccardo smiled down at her. "In fact you are very like a cat tonight, Karen, sweet-tempered and gentle, but with claws only sheathed, not blunted."

Inspiration came to her. The words she was about to say were a risk, but she was in a reckless, gambling mood.

"Are you sure you don't mean a rose?" she said. "A rose full of hidden thorns?"

He drew in his breath sharply, and she knew she was playing with fire. Then he lifted his glass to her and smiled in a way that made her heart stop.

"I salute you," he said. "Last night you understood my words. Yet you concealed this and allowed me to trap myself in a web of my own making."

"And you're not angry?"

"No, I am not angry—but I am filled with a sense of danger."

His tone was light, flirtatious, and she answered him in the same vein. "Am I dangerous?"

"You are now, *carina*. Because at last you are fighting me with a woman's weapons. They are to be feared, and when you turn them on me I wonder if I should not concede you the victory now."

With all her heart she longed to believe him sincere, but the bantering note was still there in his voice, warning her that nothing about this man was to be taken at its face value. So she laughed and said, "I remember when you were too certain of victory, Riccardo. Perhaps now you envisage defeat too easily."

"I was not so much contemplating defeat as . . . honourable surrender." He sat down beside her, but she would not look at him directly.

"Is surrender ever honourable?" she fenced.

"A man need not be ashamed of laying down his arms before a respected foe—for the right reasons. Why will you not look at me, Karen?"

The turbulent glint in his eyes would be her undoing. She must hide from him. So she looked out of the window and spoke lightly,

"Must we be foes?"

"I think we shall always be—shall we say, duelists? There will be many things between us—passion, joy, pain, even perhaps love. Who knows? But peace—never. We two were not made to be peaceful lovers."

She shrugged. "Perhaps we were not made to be lovers at all."

"You do not truly believe that, not now." He leaned forward and his fingers gently forced her face towards him. "Not now," he repeated.

No, she didn't believe it at this moment, while his touch was flooding her body with a surge of delight that shook her to the roots. She let him draw her into his arms and yielded herself to the exquisite sensation his lips could evoke. His kiss was deep and devouring, and when he had drawn her pliant body against his own hard warmth he held her very still for a long, heart-stopping moment. Then he began a leisurely exploration of her mouth that set her pulses racing with its tantalising slowness. Her fingers caressed the back of his neck before sliding upwards to wind into his thick black hair. She pulled him closer, never wanting him to stop the long, demanding kiss that told her of his own overpowering hunger for her. Wildfire coursed through her veins as his hand began to trace the curved outline of her hip, her waist, her full breasts. He drew his thumb lazily across the nipples, sending waves of tormenting sweetness through her.

His fingers had reached the high neck of the jersey dress, which came all the way up to her throat. He unlocked his mouth from hers and drew back a little, a grimace of impatience on his face.

"I preferred the way you were dressed last night," he said huskily. "Tonight you've become demure again. But it's a pretence, Karen. Your body is not demure. It tells me another story."

"Riccardo . . . please . . ." Sanity was returning, and with it the horrified realisation of how quickly she had forgotten her own warnings. She pushed him away.

He was frowning. "Playing with me, Karen?" he asked in a quiet, angry voice.

"No, of course not, it's just—it's rather early and I really am very hungry—" She was furious with herself for sounding like a gauche schoolgirl, but all her composure seemed to have deserted her. Every nerve in her body was roused and alert, tormented with unfulfilled longing, but she would force herself to distrust Riccardo no matter what it cost her.

Riccardo was watching her with cool, ironic eyes. At last he spoke lightly, "Of course. What am I thinking about to keep you waiting?"

As they were only one floor up, they walked down the stairs. On the landing was a full-length mirror, giving Karen a perfect view of them both as they descended. She was glad now that she had dressed up. It would never do to look dowdy beside Riccardo's magnificence. His pale pink evening shirt was heavily frilled and embroidered down the front, and he wore a wine-red velvet bow tie. As before, the use of slightly feminine colours and decorations only served to emphasise his stark masculinity. The shirt was tailored so that it clung to his body, revealing the lines of muscles and the colour of the tan beneath the thin material.

She was relieved to notice that Riccardo seemed to have recovered his temper. On the drive he made small talk about indifferent things, as though the scene in the hotel had never taken place. The restaurant he took her to was on a roof, six floors up, and from their table near the edge they could look out over the city as it sank into darkness and the lights glowed.

While they waited for their aperitifs to be served, Karen leaned back and enjoyed the view. She did not know that her face had softened or that the graceful lines of her body lay with a sleepy languor that caused the man beside her to draw a sharp breath. When she looked up after a few moments she found his eyes on her.

"How beautiful you are, Karen, when you allow yourself to relax long enough to stop fighting the world."

"I don't fight the world," she said with a little smile. "Just you."

"Forgive me, but I do not think that is true. I believe you were fighting before you met me. Did you ever think that if you could learn to like and trust men you might not feel you had to overcome them all the time?"

She hesitated before saying, "I learned to distrust them long before I was in a position to do battle."

"You learned that from my father?" he said with a frown.

"No, from mine."

He made a slight movement of interest. "Tell me, please."

"There isn't much to tell. He left my mother when I was a little girl. I remember how she cried, and I hated him. About two years later he came back, and she allowed him to. I just didn't see how she could do it."

"Perhaps she loved him enough to forgive him?" Riccardo suggested gently.

"But how could she ever trust him again? I couldn't. And in the end he went away for good. They got a divorce that time."

"But your mother did not become bitter. Could you not have tried to learn from her?"

"How do you know she didn't become bitter?"

"Because if she had, my father would never have loved her," he said simply.

"I don't think he treated her all that well, either. Even when he wasn't there he tried to rule her."

She told him the story of Sandra's photography, the quarrel and the streams of red roses. He threw back his head and laughed. It was a rich, attractive sound.

"That sounds just like Papa," he said at last.

"He never really gave up," said Karen wryly. "My mother held out against him no matter how much he stormed and raged, but it was a running battle between them almost to the end."

"My father was possessive," said Riccardo, "selfish, if you like. But he did not think less of people for standing up to him. And I will tell you something that may surprise you—he was proud of your mother's ability."

"I can't believe that," she said flatly. "If you could have heard him—"

"I *did* hear him. I heard what he said about her when neither of you were present. He admired what she had done in building her business up from nothing, the way she had faced the world and emerged victorious. It was exactly what he had done himself."

"Well, it's a pity he never told her that he felt that."

"Perhaps he did—in other ways than words."

"It still seems to me that he demanded everything of her and gave comparatively little of himself."

"He gave his life for you," he said with a brooding look. "Isn't that enough?"

"Do you honestly believe that?" she said quickly.

"Karen, in all my life I only once remember seeing my father weep. And that was the day he returned to this country after her funeral. He was an Italian, not one of your cold-blooded Englishmen, but a man of much feeling. When he loved a woman he *really* loved her. She became vitally necessary to him. He may not have been able to make her the centre of his world, but he made her the centre of his heart. He was only in his sixties, and a fit man for his age. But from the day of her death a heaviness descended on him. That heart attack was his first, and it killed him."

Karen said nothing. It confused her to have Alfonso presented to her in this new light. She had seen him as a selfish, demanding tyrant—albeit a loving one—a man totally sure of himself and his right to dominate his woman's life. Now, looking through Riccardo's eyes, she saw how that apparent confidence might have masked a deep fear. Sandra, she realised suddenly, had never been afraid. She had called his bluff over her career, and she had won because he didn't dare take the risk of losing her. And when he had lost her he had died—quite literally—of a broken heart.

From the look on Riccardo's face she guessed he had read her thoughts, and his next words confirmed it.

"Tell me, if my father had died first, do you believe your mother would have followed him within the year?"

"No," she said slowly. "She'd have carried on somehow."

"Well then." His hands made an eloquent gesture of finality.

She was glad that the waiter's arrival saved her from having to answer this. She needed time to sort out her thoughts. While the first course was being served and the wine poured, she said, "Why didn't your mother want to live here? If her family came from these parts . . ."

He shrugged. "Rome was a place she'd always dreamed of. I think her family connections meant more to my father than they did to her. They were a sign that he'd moved up in the world. He was proud to be a peasant, but he did not wish his children to be peasants. He was delighted when Gigi and I took after my mother's people rather than his own."

"You talk as if they came from two different countries."

"In a way they did. The Far North and the Deep South of Italy are so unlike that they should never have been united as one country. Up here the people are like the other Europeans, tall and sometimes fair-haired, because once Austria ruled this region. But the 'toe' of Italy, where my father comes from, is much closer to Africa. In old times it was raided by the Greeks, the Saracens and the Moors. Now the people are swarthy and stocky, and more like Arabs than Europeans.

"So my parents' children are all mongrels. Giulietta is the lucky one because in her the mixture shows in her appearance rather than in her nature. She is short like a Southerner, but her colouring comes from the North. Her character derives entirely from my father. Gigi and I take after the Lupones in appearance. The clash comes inside."

"I should have thought you, at least, were pure Lupone, inside as well as out," said Karen.

He shook his head and spoke intently. "You will never understand me if you think of me simply as a carbon copy of Lodovico. I look like him, but he was born of a long line of aristocrats on both sides. Half of me comes from peasants so poor that after the fifth child they prayed for their babies to die at birth, and so unsophisticated that they wore charms against the evil eye."

"What on earth is the evil eye?" she said incredulously.

"Don't laugh," he admonished her with a wry grin. "If you were overheard by a man with the *malocchio* he would turn it on you and you would become lame or blind."

"But you don't actually *believe* that?"

"My grandmother believed it. She wore a charm against the evil eye on her deathbed. Franca told me. It is from her that I learned about the poverty and primitive superstition of the people from whom I am partly descended."

"But, surely you're not superstitious?" said Karen in dismay.

"If you mean do I fear the evil eye or the devil that stalks at noon—no. But I am only one generation away from a primitive community that exists as it has done for hundreds of years. Its people live close to the earth, and they live with strength and passion, for these are the things you need to survive. And survival is all most of them have time for. When you are so close to starvation only the basic, elemental things count. *These* are the people I come from, people whose first concern is self-preservation. Trust no one because your neighbour is as hungry as you are. Give all you can to the church, but placate the pagan gods as well—just in case.

"Near the village where my father came from is a set of caves. Long ago the Greek raiders converted one of them into a shrine to Aphrodite, with symbols carved into the rock. It has remained in use till this day. Young couples leave offerings there in the days before their wedding. But perhaps you are too modern to understand the symbolism?"

"Aphrodite was the Greek goddess of love, wasn't she? The Romans called her Venus."

"True, but forget the Romans. Their Venus was a comparatively gentle, domestic creature. The Greeks knew better. They knew that love is not gentle, and they made their goddess a creature of passion and sometimes cruelty. She cast her savage blessing on the marriage beds of young men and women so that their union might be one of fire."

"And you say her shrine still attracts offerings? What do they hope to gain?"

"The young men ask her to grant them strength and potency. The girls ask that their husbands may be powerful lovers, capable of giving them much joy in bed."

"You mean, they actually go there together and say these things?"

"Of course not. They go separately and carry their wishes in their hearts. But each knows what the other seeks."

"Suppose a girl simply doesn't believe it and refuses to go?"

"That would be bad. Then her fiancé would know that she was not marrying him for love, but for some other reason."

"But how can anyone take all that seriously? It's prehistoric."

"I told you I come from a primitive people. When you say *prehistoric,* you are right. It has been this way since the dawn of time. The women of the South are wise. They worship Aphrodite because they know she represents their highest joy. When their men take them to bed they will know the pleasure that is like death. From it will come the life that will bring fresh happiness, and solace to their last years until true death claims them. Of a certainty they worship. They are worshipping life itself. To you these women doubtless seem old-fashioned, uneducated. But they have remembered a secret that you have never learned."

She was startled by the passion and intensity in his voice. He was not mocking her as he would have been two nights ago, but speaking of something about which he felt deeply. For the first time Karen began to understand what he meant about a clash inside. He was an international businessman with a sophisticated veneer, descended from great rulers who had been men of learning and culture. But he had also come from the primitive savagery of people who lived close to starvation and trusted the dark gods of the past. And the two heritages warred constantly within him.

"It seems to me that the South is stronger in you than the North," she said, puzzled. "And I don't understand. . . . At the meeting this morning—"

"That's quite different," he said at once. "The siting of the factory is a business decision, and I never allow those to be affected by sentiment. My attachment to the South is doubtless illogical, because I have never lived there, never lived that kind of life. Yet I have heard its voice calling to me distantly as long as I can remember. Perhaps because it was the birthplace of my father."

"You admired him very much, didn't you?"

"He filled my horizons for as long as I can remember. It was like living with a god. He was as remote as a god, too, for he was seldom at home. When I was born the firm was nothing like it is now. That was just after the war, and there were riches to be made out of our shattered country. My father was one of those who made his fortune quickly. It meant his being away most of the time. My mother explained this by saying that he was a great man, and great men could not always be with their families.

"When I saw him he seemed so big that he blotted out the sun. It was a shock to me when I grew taller than he and realised that he was actually quite a small man. His personality—his genius—was so huge that it dominated everything. I wanted only one thing in life—to join him in the firm and be a worthy son to him. He, too, looked forward to that day.

"He took me to work with him when I was fifteen, at my own urgent request. Later he sent me away to college, to take business courses so that I might understand the things he did not. But I cannot forget the day after my fifteenth birthday, when he took me into his office and said, 'You are a man now. You work with me.' I was determined to make him proud of me, and I succeeded. I gave every moment of my youth to working and studying to be what he wanted. I did not complain about that. It was what I wished. Whatever he required of me I did, except once. . . ."

His eyes had grown distant as his voice died away. He seemed to have forgotten Karen's existence. She held her breath, for she had seen in his face that same look of pain that had been there that afternoon, only this time increased a thousandfold. She felt she should turn her head away. But her heart melted within her. She longed, achingly, to touch his face and say, "Tell me. Let me comfort you." But she did not dare. He was lost in some private agony of his own, from which she was excluded, and she would incur his wrath if she reminded him that he had inadvertently revealed himself to her.

He came back to the present as though waking out of a sad dream. His manner was awkward, and he would not meet Karen's eyes. Instinct born of love told her that he was ashamed, that he could not endure the idea of having revealed his deepest feelings. To protect him she began to chatter aimlessly.

"You mean Innoccino, I suppose. Well, we agreed that subject was closed, didn't we? As you say, it was only a pinprick. This wine is delicious. May I have a little more?"

"I'm glad you like it. It comes from this region, and the northern wines tend to be a little lighter than those of the South. They're not to everyone's taste. I think we should have another bottle. Waiter . . ."

He had begun speaking mechanically, but gradually his voice became more normal. Karen sensed his relief as he slid away from the dangerous subject, taking the escape route she had offered him. She knew that Innoccino was not the answer. That old mistake might irritate him, but it would never have the power to bring that look of hell to his face. No, the truth was something else. But Riccardo did not trust her enough to tell her. It would remain a mystery.

"Does Gigi feel it too," she asked, "this inner clash between your mother's and father's people?"

"Gigi?" He gave a short, contemptuous laugh. "Who knows what goes on in his mind? Don't waste your time on him, Karen."

"I know he's very unhappy."

"So he's been crying on your shoulder, has he? Don't expect me to expend any pity on my brother. If he is unhappy it is poor recompense for the misery he has caused others. And he has only himself to blame for his present state. A little courage on his part would have been enough."

"He told me last night he wanted to be an opera singer. Would he have made one?"

"He has a fine voice, it is true. What he lacks is the determination. He could not stand up to our parents and demand the life that was right for himself. I was happy doing my father's work, but if I had not been, I should have defied him. If necessary I should have left his house. I would have starved, but I would have done what *I* wanted. I should not have stayed and eaten his bread and hated him in secret.

"I did the best I could for Gigi when I persuaded my father to buy the recording company and give it into his charge. Gigi now travels the world on an expense account—visiting opera houses, hearing singers, signing them. He has a lovely time."

"But he doesn't want to listen to others," she said. "He wants to be onstage singing himself. It's probably worse for him this way because he sees other people living the life he wanted. You're so patriarchal, Riccardo. You buy him a company, pat him on the head and say you've done your best for him, as though it were up to you to arrange his life. But it isn't."

"Then let him get out and try now," Riccardo flared. "He's only twenty-seven. That's not too old to start. But he won't do it because he's past making any effort. The rot's gone too deep. He prefers to stay and gamble and sponge on my mother. A man who allows himself to go rotten because of one disappointment is worthy of nothing but contempt. Tell me, Karen, is that what a woman wants—a man who weeps on her shoulder and goes running to her with his misfortunes, like a weakling? If you throw in your lot with Gigi, you will repent. And I say that not because I need you on my side in the firm."

"Why are you and Gigi enemies?" she said impulsively. "It's not just that you dislike each other. There's something else, isn't there?"

He was silent for a moment, his face dark.

"Yes, there's something else," he said at last in a brooding voice. "But I cannot tell you what it is. It is a private matter, and I ask you not to speak of it again."

"But shouldn't I know—if you want me on your side?"

"I will not buy your allegiance at that price," he snapped. "Please, Karen, let us drop this subject."

She was silent, hurt by his snub. After a while he laid his hand over hers and spoke in a kinder voice.

"Come, let us discuss my brother no longer. He is a dangerous subject for us. He causes us to quarrel, and that I do not wish to do." He gave her a crooked grin. "We may have to be duelists, but we can fight like gentlemen, can't we?"

She had to laugh at that, and he leaned across and kissed her lightly on the lips.

"Don't start that here," she said desperately. "I don't want to be applauded by an audience again."

"You are right. There are too many other people around us. Let us go."

They had the lift to themselves. As soon as the doors closed he took her in his arms, not kissing her, but looking down into her face with a wry, tender expression.

"I was mistaken about you," he said. "I decided the first evening that you were charming but predictable. I should have known that no woman can be both."

There was a long silence while she smiled into his eyes.

"I'll die before I ask you which one I am," she said at last.

"But you do not need to ask," he said softly.

Despite her light manner, her heart was in turmoil during the drive back to the hotel. Riccardo seemed to be taking her acquiescence for granted, and with every fibre of her being she wanted him, but still she did not trust him. She knew she was heading for something reckless and dangerous, but his vibrant physical presence had the power to silence her common sense. The only safety lay in escape, and by the end of the journey she had made a desperate decision.

When the car drew up outside the hotel she opened the passenger door quickly and ran up the stairs. She heard him call her name, but she did not look back. At the desk she claimed her key and fled up to the first floor. But when she had thrust the key into the lock, something seemed to hold her frozen, and she stayed for a moment, leaning her forehead against the door, racked with indecision. She could neither force herself on nor turn back. After a moment she heard him come up the stairs. He stood just behind her, but did not touch her.

"Why do you run away from me, Karen? I am nothing to be feared." He spoke in a quiet, sad voice that she had never heard him use before.

"I've changed my mind, that's all," she said harshly. The words sounded callous to her own ears, but she couldn't help it.

"In that case—good night." He brushed her hair aside and dropped a soft kiss on the back of her neck. And was gone.

Stunned, she looked about her in the empty hallway, but she was really alone. As always, Riccardo had done the very last thing she had expected. She sighed, telling herself that it was better this way. Then she went into her room, and slammed the door shut behind her with slightly more force than was necessary.

She pulled off her dress and flung it across the back of a chair. Her underclothes followed, and when she was naked she went into the bathroom to take a shower. She could see her body in the long mirrors. It was a beautiful body, and at the moment it yearned for the man who was on the other side of the wall. It wanted to know fulfillment in his arms, not lie in the chaste bleakness of a cold bed. But it couldn't have what it wanted. There were tears running down her face.

She stepped out of the shower and wrapped a large bath towel round her. She felt tired suddenly, a deep weariness that was emotional as much as physical. She went back into the bedroom and dropped onto the bed, lying on her back with her eyes closed.

The sound of a door made them fly open. The room was almost in darkness, lit only by a glow coming through the window. But she could clearly make out the figure of Riccardo. He had changed his clothes, and was now wearing a wild silk bathrobe. He stood just inside the bedroom door and regarded her silently for a moment.

"How did you get in here?" she demanded.

Instead of answering he moved closer and sat down on the side of the bed. There were only a few feet between them now, and his eyes held a look that made the towel feel frighteningly flimsy. Something strange was happening to her breathing.

"I used this," he said, opening his hand so that she could see the key gleaming there. "You left it in your lock."

"That was an accident. If you had the unspeakable arrogance to take it as an invitation—after what I said—"

"Hush, *cara,* do not be angry. I took it only as a sign that I might hope." He took her hand and placed the key in it, folding the fingers over.

She pulled away from him and rolled off the bed on the far side. Her pulses were racing. As she found her bag and dropped the key into it she knew she was stalling for time.

He had risen and followed her. When he stood a few feet away he loosened the belt of his robe and let it drop to the floor. He was naked. In the faint light from the window she could see the whole magnificent outline of him, lean and muscular, the broad shoulders tapering to a flat belly and narrow hips. Now there was no mistaking his desire for her.

His fingers were at her breasts, pulling at the towel where it was tucked in. A tug and it was gone. She had no will to stop him. The moment for that was past. He took her chin between his fingers so that she had to look up to him.

"If I had knocked at your door, Karen, what would you have done? Would you have sent me away?"

She shook her head, unable to speak through the hard ache in her throat.

"Shall I leave you?" he said thickly.

She swayed and fell against his hard, warm chest. She could not have sent him away now if her life had depended on it.

"Tell me," he demanded urgently. "Let me hear you say it."

"I want you to stay, Riccardo. I want you. . . ."

Her words were almost inaudible, but it was as though they had detonated an explosion. His arm encircled her waist tightly, grinding her body against his. He smothered her mouth with his own, moving with a slow insistence that robbed her of the power of thought. All the world seemed to be concentrated into the sweet, agonizing awareness of pleasure that lashed along every nerve. Tremors shook her as his hands roved and explored with feverish possessiveness. It was as though some deep instinct guided him unerringly to those places that excited her most. His lips had left hers and were caressing the little throbbing pulse at the base of her throat; he was bending her backwards so that her supple frame arched against him, and she could feel the unyielding muscles against her length.

She closed her eyes. Only her burning flesh told her now that his lips had slid downwards to the swell of her breasts, seeking the hard nipples that throbbed achingly. His tongue's lingering caresses sent shock waves surging convulsively through her, and she clasped her hands tightly behind his head, twining her fingers in the springy black hair.

Then his arm was beneath her knees and the room spun as she was lifted high in his powerful arms. She felt the coolness of the sheet beneath her as he pressed her gently down onto the bed, then drew back to take in the magnificent vision of her long, slender body, the skin pale and luminous in the darkness. He was holding himself in check, prolonging the moments of sensuous delight for them both.

"Let me look at you," he said in a voice that shook with passion. "You are made like a goddess, cruel Aphrodite."

His hand was tracing her curving contours with lazy confidence, lingering to cup one breast in the palm of his hand before sliding into the hollow of her waist and out over her full rounded hips. When she could endure no more of the tantalising delay she opened her arms to him,

"Riccardo," she whispered, "love me."

For a moment she saw his eyes blaze above her before his body covered her own. His voice muttered something hoarsely, but the words had no meaning to her. The room had vanished in swirling darkness. They were beyond space and time, their mating a primitive ritual on which the pagan gods smiled as they had done since the dawn of creation. And against sense, against reason, her whole being was becoming suffused with passionate worship, so that the meaning of the shrine became clear to her, no longer a relic of barbarous days, but a timeless outpouring of gratitude from women for the joy that linked them to life.

He was compelling her into his rhythm until she no longer knew where she ended and he began. As she plunged towards the centre of the earth she cried aloud in ecstasy and heard his muffled groans mingled with her cries as she clutched him to her. Then she wept tears of desolation as she became herself again, felt him grow apart from her and become separate. Yet he did not pull quite away but lay, panting slightly, staring at her with veiled eyes.

She rested herself on her elbow so that she could look down on him. There was something in his face that she must read. Almost she might have said it was a look of hesitancy. She looked at him intently. The primitive peasant who threw caution to the winds and claimed the woman he considered his was fading. In his place there was Riccardo again, a man too sophisticated not to be cautious, a man who did not trust her and would hide his feelings from her.

Suddenly she knew what she must do to keep that other man with her. She must do what Sandra would have done, take his face in her hands and tell him that she loved him. She could safely leave the rest to him. She touched his cheek with soft fingers and whispered his name.

"There's something I must tell you," she said.

She would tell him everything, including what she had overheard the first night. She would say she was his if only he would love her. The pressure of so many words tumbling over themselves struck her dumb for a moment.

"Riccardo, I . . ."

In the distance she heard a bell but shut it out of her mind. It was too far away to be her telephone.

"Listen to me," she said.

He still had not spoken. His eyes were fixed on hers with that strange unfathomable expression, as though doors were closing within him. He made a restless movement.

"That bell is coming from my room," he said uncertainly.

"Leave it. There's something I must say," she pleaded.

He took one of her hands and kissed it briefly.

"I can't do that, *cara.* I've never been able to ignore a telephone bell. Let me answer it, otherwise you won't have all my attention. It's important, isn't it?"

"Yes," she said sadly. "It's important."

He pushed her gently away and took up his robe.

"I'll return in two minutes." He took her face between his hands and kissed it. "You are beautiful."

It was odd how the empty place in her heart ached when he had gone. He had spoken gently and kissed her, promised to return. But there had been a lightness in his voice that told her the precious moment was gone almost beyond recall. When he returned she would never be able to say what she wanted to. The passionate feeling was dying in her, too, to be replaced by the realisation that she had been loved and abandoned—however temporarily.

With one half of her mind she heard him enter his own room next door, seize the phone and begin to speak. The next second she had frozen, and her heart was thudding so hard that it blotted out the sound of his next words. For what she had plainly heard him say was *"Alicia!"*

When the blood had ceased drumming in her ears she sat stone-still, as dead and rigid as a statue on a pagan altar. She could still hear his voice, though not the separate words. But the tone was enough. It was soft, affectionate, anxious. And it went on and on. Clearly he had forgotten his promise to return quickly.

At last she could move. She rose painfully to her feet and went to the open door that led into the corridor. As Riccardo had also left his door open, she was able to catch odd words in Italian.

"Don't cry, my darling. . . . Of course I will come to you. . . . Immediately . . . I can be home in three hours. . . . No, I am not angry that you called. Why should I be? You know that you can call me anywhere in the world, and I will always come to you. . . . My darling, who else do I love but you?"

Mechanically Karen closed the door and leaned against it, her heart turned to ice. Her whole being was now nothing but a silent prayer of thanks that this had happened before she had uttered the words of love that would have made Riccardo laugh at her forever. There was no room at the moment for pain and humiliation at the way he could rise from their ecstatic union to go to another woman. That would come later, she knew that. But by then she would be far away from here, far from anywhere where she needed to see Riccardo's face.

The thoughts galvanised her into action. She began to throw on her clothes, choosing those she had arrived in today. Some part of her mind that could remain unfeeling and efficient in the face of agony told her to check her purse. Yes, there was the English credit card that was also accepted in Italy. It would buy her a ticket at Milan Airport. If only she had her passport on her. She could have gone straight back to England. As it was, she would have to return first to Rome and chance a meeting with Riccardo. But with any luck he'd be as anxious as she was to avoid a meeting—after he'd read the note she was going to leave him.

When she was dressed she seated herself at a little desk by the window and drew forward the pad of hotel notepaper. In just this place and in just this way she had sat earlier this afternoon to write to him about the champagne. Her throat constricted at the thought, and tears began to pour down her cheeks. But she forced herself on until she could read the words she had written.

It isn't only women who cannot be both charming and predictable. My departure in this way can leave you in no doubt as to which one I found you. K.

She folded the paper into an envelope, wrote his name on the outside and laid it on her pillow. She walked quietly down the stairs and out into the dark streets. After ten minutes walking she found a taxi and directed it to Milan Airport. Only when she had collapsed into the backseat could she bury her face in her hands and give way to the sobs that were wracking her.

Chapter Eight

The young woman who walked into the lobby of Rome's most expensive hotel a month later had an air of assurance that made her stand out even in this establishment. Her soft beige dress hung loosely about her slim body, its style a masterpiece of costly simplicity. Her bare arms glowed with a deep golden tan, and when she pulled off the dark glasses her eyes had been transformed to an almost unnaturally deep blue by the tan of her face. Her step was light and firm as she approached the reception desk.

"I have a suite booked for tonight," she said. "My name is Karen Conway."

"Certainly signorina," the girl receptionist beamed. "The same suite that you had before. The car was satisfactory?"

"Perfectly, thank you. In four weeks it never gave me a moment's trouble."

The girl hunted in a row of pigeon holes and produced two slips of paper.

"These are telephone messages for you, signorina. Signora Bonnicelli requests you to call her as a matter of the utmost urgency. Three times today she has called to ask if you have arrived. And Signor Tornese has called twice. He asks that you contact him at this number."

Karen's heart gave a painful jolt before she could control it. She stared at the paper she was holding, on which Gigi's telephone number was written, and tried to deaden the anguish that swept through her. Of course the message was from Gigi. She had called him several times during the month she had been away, driving aimlessly from place to place, enjoying the feeling that no one in the world knew exactly where she was. Gigi alone knew the day she was due to arrive back in Rome, and the name of her hotel. He must have told his sister. But why was Giulietta so anxious to talk to her?

When the porter had deposited her bags in her suite and bowed himself out over her generous tip, she looked round and breathed a sigh of relief at finding herself alone. Now that there were no eyes to see, the air of superb self-confidence seemed to fall away from her like a garment she no longer needed.

This was the second time she had stayed in this suite at the Hotel Garibaldi. The first time had been a month ago when she had fled here to avoid Riccardo. For two nights she had sobbed herself to sleep, reliving every searing moment of the love that had taken her to such ecstatic heights, and the brutal treachery that had immediately plunged her into the depths of despair.

Why had she not gone straight back to England, as she had at first intended? Perhaps because it would have been a defeat, and defeat was something she could not accept?

She had caught an early morning flight from Milan to Rome, and jumped into a taxi to take her to the villa. There she found Gigi, sitting downstairs having breakfast alone. The sight made her pull herself together.

"I found your brother's overbearing ways more than I could take," she had said in answer to his raised eyebrows.

"You mean, you left Rik in Milan?" said Gigi, wide-eyed.

"I've no idea where he is," she said truthfully.

"Well, he's not here." Gigi had regarded her curiously, and under his penetrating gaze she became aware that her face was probably swollen from weeping, and she must look untidy. Those catlike eyes, as perceptive as a woman's, suddenly terrified her. But there was only sympathy in his voice when he said, "I understand, *cara*. Rik isn't used to ladies who say no. I expect he turned nasty. You did well to leave."

She had said nothing for the moment. Let Gigi think that if he wanted to. Let him think anything but the truth. After a few mouthfuls of coffee she felt calmer, and managed to speak in a casual voice.

"You've no idea where he is then? I thought he might have come back."

"Possibly. There would be no point in him remaining once you had left, would there?" Gigi's voice was filled with glee."I congratulate you, *cara*. For this I can even forgive you for what you did to me."

"Done? What have I—?" Karen stared at him blankly. Then the memory had come back to her. Yesterday morning, the board meeting, the vote—it was as distant as a tale told from another planet. Had it really been only twenty-four hours ago?

"You've forgotten all about it," said Gigi reproachfully. "You shatter my life, grind my hopes into the dust, and your memory bears not the slightest imprint. Fickle woman."

He had ended with a melodramatic flourish that would not have been out of place on the stage. At any other time Karen would have enjoyed the performance, but now she was too emotionally wrung out to do anything but stare at him. She had wept unrestrainedly in the darkness of the taxi, but once aboard the plane she had forced herself to be calm before the other passengers. The strain of fighting back her sobs throughout the flight had brought a hard pain to her throat that was still there.

One thought had penetrated her misery. Riccardo had not returned to the villa, or contacted his family. If she got out quickly she could avoid meeting him. But a great lethargy seemed to have taken possession of her.

"I daresay you had your reasons, *cara,*" Gigi had said cheerfully. He seemed to have decided to forget his shattered life, but his eyes still had that piercing quality. "I forgive you. Tell me what you are going to do now."

"You were right about my not staying here, Gigi. I want to leave now, this minute."

"It will take a little longer than that to obtain an apartment for you. In the meantime I suggest a hotel. I will take you there myself."

He had been all solicitude. While Karen packed he had gone and talked to his mother. She had been dreading the moment when she must face the signora and find a way to explain her abrupt departure, but a few minutes later the signora floated into her room, wearing a dressing gown, and gave her an affectionate embrace.

"I understand, signorina. Gigi has explained everything to me. Of course you must do what you think is right."

Karen's halting apologies were cut short by the signora's effusiveness. Gigi had stood in the doorway watching the scene like the cat that has swallowed the cream. It was all too obvious, Karen thought, what 'explanation' he had offered, and it was probably the best one. Riccardo was unlikely ever to contradict it with the truth.

Gigi had driven her into Rome and saw her installed in the Hotel Garibaldi. As soon as she was alone she had cried herself to sleep.

She had loved him. She had given him the best she had. And he had turned from her cynically to go to another woman. The only consolation she could offer herself was the reflection that she had left him in a way that would gall his pride. But it was no comfort at all. It eased slightly the sting of humiliation, but did nothing to mend her breaking heart.

When she had awakened it was almost evening. She felt better for the rest, and with the return of her strength some of her fighting spirit also came back. It had never been her way to turn tail and run from a battlefield. She had merely retreated to regroup her forces. She would not return to England and leave Riccardo a clear winner.

There had been a message to say that Gigi had rung and left a number for her to call back. She called and arranged to meet him for dinner. Over drinks he had told her that there was no news from his brother, all the time watching her face carefully. But she had been expecting his scrutiny and met it with a brightly blank face. She had also fended off his delicately worded queries until at last he seemed to give up.

"All right," she said suddenly, "I'll have that apartment. I can't live in a hotel all the time. How long will it take to fix it?"

"A few weeks. Things move slowly in Italy. We are a nation of bureaucrats. . . ."

"I don't want to stay here for the next few weeks. Can you handle it for me, please, Gigi?"

"Certainly I can. Are you proposing to give me—" he had hesitated and emphasised the next word very slightly "—full powers to act for you?"

His face was as bland and innocent as a baby's, but he didn't fool her.

"Yes," she said firmly. "You can vote my shares while I'm away."

His eyes gleamed. She had turned away so as not to see it. She was sick at heart.

The following day Gigi had accompanied her first to a bank, then to the company lawyer. The bank manager was happy to arrange all the credit she needed to live independently until her new wealth made itself available in hard cash. At the lawyer's office she had signed papers that transferred control of her property to Gigi. Coming out into the sunlight afterwards she compressed her lips and stared straight ahead, ignoring Gigi's triumphant face. It was done—for good or ill. She refused to think which it might be.

The hotel had arranged the hire of a car for her, and she left the next morning. Gigi came to see her off, and also to impart the news that there was still no word from Riccardo.

She had gone North, stopping wherever her fancy took her. She had her cameras, and Italy was a photographer's paradise. She had lingered in Florence and Pisa, then driven on to Bologna. There she headed east to see Venice.

With one superficial part of her mind she had enjoyed herself. The sun was hot and the wine sweet. In cities she had stayed in grand hotels where, at a price, her every wish was treated as an imperious command. Otherwise she stopped in tiny wayside *trattorias* with just one room to let and ate her meals with the family. She had enjoyed both equally. Italy ravished her senses, and she was quickly drunk with beauty.

But at night she could no longer escape the rending of her heart. There was a desolate emptiness within her that it seemed nothing would ever fill. She had yearned to go back to catch one glimpse of Riccardo, to hear his voice again, feel his touch. Night after night she would wake, weeping, her body wracked with anguish.

The future stretched before her, a bleak empty road to the end of her life, with nothing of joy or brightness in it. For Riccardo had changed her. The woman who had known searing ecstatic love in his arms could never go back to being the half-awakened girl she had been before.

For the first time in years she had found herself thinking of Jake. Jake had been a young actor she'd met when she was nineteen. She'd rushed headlong into love with him, too young and starry-eyed to see that he was an equally good actor offstage as on. He'd acted his way into her heart, into her bed and, when it suited him, out of her life.

When he was in London she spent nights with him in his dingy bed-sitter. When he was doing repertory in the provinces she listened for the phone. After a year he'd rung her from Newcastle to say he wasn't returning to London at all. He and another actor were going to try their luck in America. He'd sold his old car to pay for his ticket, so she did understand that he couldn't come back to say good-bye, didn't she?

Sandra had confined herself to the comment, "It couldn't have been an impulsive decision. You need a visa for America. He must have planned it weeks ago."

Looking back, Karen was grateful for the brutal selfishness that had caused Jake to dump her when she no longer had a role to play in his life. It had helped her get him into perspective. But at the time she had felt that her heart was broken and would stay broken for ever.

It hadn't. It had mended surprisingly quickly. Now she knew why. Nothing she had experienced in a year with Jake could compare with the blinding ecstasy she had known in one night in Riccardo's arms. In those days she had thought herself a woman of the world. Now she saw herself as an infatuated girl, almost as naive when her love affair ended as when it began. Riccardo had stripped away her pretences and shown her to herself as a deeply passionate woman. He had left his mark on her, and she would never be the same. There would be no swift recovery this time. If she never saw Riccardo again, she would be deeply his to the end of her days.

It was in Venice that she had first begun to realise that the situation might no longer be under her own control. She had waited another week, wandering the little alleys of the city on the water, taking roll after roll of film. Afterwards, when she looked at those pictures, she couldn't remember having taken them, or even having been in those places. For the whole week she had functioned as an automaton while her mind echoed with the nagging, insistent question whose answer would decide her whole life.

Finally she had called Gigi, told him she would be in Rome within two days and would like him to reserve her a suite at the Garibaldi, and had replaced the receiver before he could ask questions.

And now here she was, four weeks and a lifetime away from the girl who had left a month ago. The sight of her own eyes in the mirror dismayed her. They had a new ruthlessness that had not been there before. Well, she would need to be ruthless now. With every day that passed she grew more certain of it.

She called Giulietta first and was startled at the passionate relief in the girl's voice over the phone. What on earth could have happened to get her into this state?

"Karen *please*, I must talk to you *now*. And not on the telephone."

"Come over here then. I'll wait for you. But, Giulietta —what on earth is wrong?"

"I cannot speak now. But I need your help desperately. I will be with you in half an hour."

She arrived in twenty minutes and flung her arms round Karen. It was not so much a welcome as a desire to reassure herself that Karen had really arrived. Her face was pale and strained.

"Grazie, grazie, carissima," she whispered tearfully. "Without you I die."

Karen was shocked by the change in her. In her mind Giulietta was always a carefree, sunny little doll. But here was a distraught woman who twisted a handkerchief between her fingers as she talked and seemed permanently on the verge of tears. Karen made her drink a glass of wine, then settled down to listen to her.

"Pietro has been away this last few weeks. I don't go

with him this time. There is just me and Maria, and we are no good together. Always fights and arguments. She stays out late and won't tell me where she is or who she is with. Then I find out she is seeing Gigi. This I will not have. I do not like her, but she is Pietro's daughter. I must protect her. But what can I do? He is my brother. He is rotten, but how can I say this? She tells me she is in love with him? In love! How does she know? She is a child."

"I think you must tell Pietro what you think of Gigi, even if he is your brother," said Karen. "Then he can protect Maria."

"But I can't do that." Giulietta's voice rose to a wail. "Maria make threats. She says she will tell Pietro . . . something about me . . ."

Karen saw light. "Is it about the man who telephoned the day Gigi and I were there?"

"*Si.* You know . . . ?"

"I couldn't help hearing what you were saying. You'd arranged to meet him for lunch, and you couldn't because we were there. You called him *caro.* It had to be a man."

"Maria has found out. She says she will tell Pietro. This I could not endure. I love my husband, Karen. I do not love Enrico—not really *love*—but he is young and strong, and Pietro is old before his time."

Karen sighed. She could neither approve Giulietta's behaviour nor wholly condemn it. She was too fond of her for that.

Giulietta raised a tear-stained face. "Help me, Karen, I beseech you—or I jump into the river."

"Well, I'm going to help you, so we needn't think of that," Karen said, trying to rally her with a light voice. "What must I do?"

"You will see Enrico for me? You will tell him it must be broken off? I cannot meet him again myself . . . is too dangerous."

"Can't you just phone him?"

The little blond head shook vigorously. "I can't. He

wouldn't accept it on the phone. He would not believe . . . he will try to see me. Besides—" she hesitated and a tender look spread over her face "—I cannot do that to him. He is a nice boy. He loves me, I think. He deserves more than a phone call. That is why—" she fumbled in her bag and brought out a sealed envelope "—I have written him this. You will give it to him, *si?*"

"Giulietta, are you mad—giving him a letter when you're trying to break it off! Have you said anything dangerous in it?"

"I have assured him of my love forever," the girl said solemnly. "That is being kind to him, so he will leave me alone."

For a moment Karen contemplated explaining to Giulietta that her logic was at fault, but gave it up almost immediately. She wouldn't have understood a word.

"When and where am I to meet him?" she said, resigned.

"Tonight. There is a *trattoria* called Passacaglia in the Via Sistina. He is expecting to see me there at eight."

"All right, Giulietta, I'll do what you want. Now, dry your tears. There's nothing to worry about. Maria can't prove anything if you bluff it out."

Giulietta threw her arms round Karen again and kissed her.

"*Grazie, grazie!* You save me. Now I must go. *Addío, cara.*"

She was gone like a little blond whirlwind. Karen sat looking at the thick envelope. In her present state Giulietta's behaviour was incomprehensible. For Karen, love and passionate desire were both bound up in one man. How could you divide them between two men in such a way?

But it was not her business to condemn. She had promised to help, and she would. After that she hoped Giulietta would have the sense to keep out of scrapes. But she doubted it.

She called Gigi, who was effusively glad to hear from her. Her new apartment was ready. She could sign the lease that very afternoon and take possession tomorrow. She told Gigi she would be with him at once and hurried out for a taxi.

She found the block of flats easily. It was a relatively modern building in the centre of the city, in a small road off the Via Nazionale. She took the lift to the third floor and knocked on the door of Gigi's apartment. He opened at once.

"You've been away a long time, *cara,*" he said reproachfully when he had given her coffee. "I was worried about you. So was brother Rik. At least—he was worried in case you never came back and I had your shares forever."

"I gather you've been enjoying your power to the full," she said.

"I voted against the land acquisition in Milan. He was as mad as fire." Gigi snickered in pleased remembrance. "And now the option's run out, so we've lost the retainer. That's going to take some explaining in the books. How clever of you to ferret it out."

Karen passed a hand over her eyes. In the turmoil of her heart she had barely given a thought to the land that had taken her on that disastrous trip to Milan in the first place. Now, through her ignorance and interference, the firm had suffered a major loss. Which was exactly what Riccardo had warned her would happen.

Gigi sat looking at her, as delighted as a small boy who'd put a stone in someone's shoe and heard them yell. Only he wasn't a small boy. He was a grown man, at least outwardly. Inside he was so stunted as to be almost an infant, with an infant's inability to see beyond himself or to work out the consequences of his actions.

She pulled herself together. The sooner she put right her mistake the better.

"Well, I'm back now," she said with a bright smile. "I can start being clever on my own account."

For a barely perceptible moment Gigi's grin seemed to freeze on his lips. Then the moment passed, and he was himself again. Karen wondered if she had only imagined the desperate look in his eyes.

"You mean, I take it, that you want your shares back?" he said cheerfully. "There's no hurry, is there? Get settled in to your flat first, and we'll go along to the lawyer next week."

She eyed him suspiciously. "When's the next board meeting, Gigi?"

"There isn't one. Rik's away at the moment. He said he'd set the date when he returned."

"Away?" A cold hand seemed to clutch at Karen's heart. "Where is he? And when is he coming back?"

"The answer to both questions is I don't know. I honestly don't."

"He can't just have vanished without telling anyone where he was going or when he was coming back," she said.

"Why not? You did. I got three phone calls from unnamed places. And the last one was two days ago to say you wanted me to book your hotel. I still don't know where you've been for the last four weeks. I kept telling everyone I didn't know where you were, but they wouldn't believe me." His voice became petulant. "It was like the Inquisition. They seemed to think if they asked me the same questions every day I'd give in and admit I knew something."

She felt as though she was choking with hope. "Everyone?" she managed to say. "Who?"

"I tell you everyone," he said sulkily. "My mother was concerned for you because you were a foreign girl driving alone through Italy and might come to harm. Franca was worried in case you weren't eating enough. And recently Giulietta has been nagging me about you. God knows why!"

"I see," she said faintly. She felt as though something

had died within her. Fiercely she called herself a fool. Eventually she managed to calm the storm of disappointment and speak calmly.

"When did Riccardo leave?"

"About a week after you did. We had the meeting to decide about the land." Gigi gave another vengeful chuckle. "He didn't know I had your proxy vote. The company rules say a decision can be made by a majority vote of the shareholders present at any one meeting, so if one of them is absent it doesn't matter. He'd persuaded Mama to vote with him about the land, so he'd have had a majority if I'd been voting only my own shares. You should have seen his face when he discovered I had yours. He'd have liked to kill me."

"Or me," Karen murmured.

"He left the next day, without saying where he was going. But I saw his jacket lying over a chair with his passport sticking out of an inner pocket. So I suppose he's abroad."

Karen felt sick with dismay. This was the one thing she'd never thought of, and it could be a disaster. If he took a long time coming back—she became cold all over.

"I expect Lisa would know where he is," said Gigi. "I haven't asked her. It's so pleasant without him."

Karen's nails ground into her palms. Nothing in the world would make her go to Riccardo's secretary asking to be told his whereabouts and see the curiosity creep into those discreet eyes.

"Well—" Gigi stood up "—if you've finished your coffee, I'll take you up to your apartment."

She followed him up to the fourth floor and into the rooms he had taken for her. The decorations and furnishings were modern and simple, with an austere beauty that she liked immediately.

Gigi spoke into the telephone, and within a few minutes the agent arrived with a lease for her to sign. She did so mechanically, and when he had gone she sat down in one of the big armchairs and stretched out.

"I love it," she said. "Thank you, Gigi."

He gave her the look of beaming childlike pleasure that she was learning to distrust. "Yes, Rik thought it was rather nice too," he said.

She jumped up as though stung and began to pace the room.

"You mean—this apartment used to be Riccardo's?"

"I told you he had one in this building. What difference does it make?"

She pulled up sharply. "None really," she managed to say with a shrug.

"Do you really hate him all that much?"

"I don't hate him. I'm perfectly indifferent to him," she said sharply.

"But you don't want to sleep in the bed where he took his girl friends, is that it?"

"I've told you I don't care about Riccardo or his girl friends," she snapped. "He can do what he likes; it's no concern of mine." Then a sudden inspiration came to her, and she added, "I don't even care about Alicia."

She would die before she asked anyone outright about Alicia. But this oblique method might produce results. She held her breath. Gigi was looking at her oddly.

"Who told you about Alicia?" he said at last.

"Does it matter, as long as I know?"

"I suppose not. But it's strange—I can't see Rik just telling you. He never talks about her to anyone. He doesn't discuss the things he feels deeply about, and if there's one person on earth that he loves, it's her," said Gigi quietly.

The pain was almost unbearable. She took a deep breath and tried to still the violent beating of her heart.

"Do you know her?" she managed to say.

"Not really. I haven't seen her for years. Rik keeps her to himself."

"They've been together a long time then?"

"About ten years."

She gave a high, unnatural laugh. "Well, you said he was a faithless husband. It seems that he was a faithless lover as well, if he had Alicia and all the other girls too."

"Well, what Rik wants, he takes," said Gigi slowly.

"Yes," she said in deep bitterness of soul. "Oh, yes."

She knew she must have given herself away now, but she was past caring. She could no longer endure the torment of ignorance.

"The one I feel sorry for is his wife," she said, trying to regain her calm tone. "Ten years . . . she must have known."

"Known? Of course she knew. Dear Karen, why do you imagine she killed herself?"

"Killed herself?"

"Didn't you know? I thought you must; you seem so well informed."

She stared at him, dumb with misery.

"Lucia drowned herself," he went on, looking at her. "They found her in a river in the grounds of the villa, but by then it had been too late for a long time."

"The villa?" she said through frozen lips. "You mean—?"

"The one in the hills. Riccardo still owns it. You'd have thought he'd get rid of it as quickly as possible, wouldn't you? But it's just the right place for Alicia; so secluded and private, he can have her all to himself."

She staggered as though someone had struck her. Gigi's hand was under her arm as he tried to lead her to a chair, but she pulled herself together and escaped from him. She could not endure his touch. In fact, she couldn't endure his presence another moment. She didn't want to hear any more; it was too horrible.

"I've kept you too long," she said. "Thank you for

finding me the apartment, Gigi. I shall move in tomorrow. I must go back to the hotel now. I'm going out tonight, and I want to rest first."

She said this to make it plain to him that she could not dine with him, but he did not mention the matter, or attempt to detain her. Nor did he offer to drive her back to the hotel, which at any other time she might have thought strange. But now her mind was occupied with just one thought—to get away from him as quickly as possible. In the street she walked away from the building at a hurried pace, despite the heat. Eventually she managed to hail a taxi and sank gratefully into the back seat. But she did not weep this time. She was past weeping.

She slept the afternoon away. It was easy to sleep. It was only people with feelings who were wakeful, she discovered. Those whose hearts had turned to stone within them slept easily. She was glad. What she had to do would be less complicated now that her love was dead.

By eight o'clock that evening she was standing outside the *trattoria*, with Giulietta's envelope in her hand, wishing she hadn't got herself mixed up in that foolish young woman's business. But it was too late now.

She knew the boy as soon as she saw him. He sat close to the door and looked up eagerly whenever anyone came in. The disappointment that washed over his face marked him as a lover. He was in his middle twenties with a sulky, immature face. When Karen approached his table he gave her a courteous smile.

"Signorina, please—if you will be so kind—I am expecting a friend; this seat is taken."

"You are Enrico?"

"Yes, but how—?"

"Giulietta sent me." Karen seated herself. "She can't come, I'm afraid. She asked me to give you this." She handed him the letter. While he read it she ordered herself a pizza and some red wine. When they came Enrico looked up at the waiter, his eyes blazing in a white face.

"*Strega,*" he ordered curtly.

Sandra had kept *strega* for Alfonso, and Karen had tried it once. It was liquid fire and deadly potent. Every time Enrico emptied his glass he ordered another, until he reached the end of the long letter. Then he threw the pages down on the table, and his mouth twisted with bitterness.

"She is rich; I am poor; she has done with me. There is no more to be said."

"No," said Karen urgently. "It isn't like that. She's afraid in case her husband should find out. Does she say in the letter that she loves you?"

"She says many things. She says the things rich women say when they have no more use for a man. But the loudest of all, she says she will never see me again."

"I'm sorry," said Karen lamely.

He poured the yellow liquid down his throat, and the waiter refilled his glass. She could see that he would not stay in command of himself much longer. He was looking at her with tipsy solemnity.

"I do not ask who you are, signorina. It is enough that you are the dark angel, sent to blast my life. It is right that you do not have a name."

"My name is Karen. I'm a friend of Giulietta's. She thought I could explain to you why she can no longer see you . . . make it easier—"

"*Easier?*" His voice rose to a shrill note, and she looked round her uneasily. "One day, perhaps someone you love will betray you, and then you will discover whether words can make it easier."

"I'm sorry," she said at once. "You're quite right."

He saw her looking round again and laughed mirthlessly.

"Do I embarrass you? Then let us go. I can be drunk in the street as well as here."

As the waiter approached she felt for her bag, but he stopped her with grave dignity.

"Thank you, signorina, but no. When I said I was poor it was not for that reason. No woman pays for me—not even the dark angel."

She followed him out into the street, wondering helplessly what to do with him. To leave him alone in this state was obviously impossible. She understood why Giulietta had said he was a nice boy. Superficially he might seem a *gigolo,* but Karen sensed that his feelings were sincere, probably more sincere than those of the girl who had dumped him when he grew to be inconvenient.

They wandered in and out of two more wine bars. Enrico's eyes grew blacker all the time, but he seemed steady enough on his feet. He was talking of Giulietta in a rambling way. Karen had a feeling that she was in streets where she had been before, but she had to give all her attention to Enrico.

"She does not mean it," he was saying. "She will see me again; she must."

"No, Enrico, she really can't. It's much too dangerous—"

"I tell you she will," he almost shouted. "This letter is a trick, to make me love her more. She would never . . . she would never . . ."

To Karen's horror his face crumpled like a child's, and the next moment he was sitting down on the pavement, his head in his hands, sobbing. Karen knelt beside him and put her arms round him.

"I loved her," he wailed. "How can she do this to me? I wanted her to come away with me."

After a while his sobbing grew quieter, and he allowed Karen to help him to his feet. He clung on to her as though to a mother.

"You are in need of assistance, signorina?"

Karen jumped at the sound of the powerful, gravelly voice that came from behind her. There stood a large, middle-aged man, who looked vaguely familiar.

"I . . . need a taxi . . . to get my friend home," she said.

"Your friend? That one there is your friend?" The man gave Enrico a derisive look. "That one is no friend to a decent woman."

"He is *my* friend," said Karen angrily. All her protective instincts were suddenly roused for the boy still weeping hopelessly on her shoulder. "He's my friend, and I want to help him."

The man gave her a fatherly look. "Best you get rid of him," he advised. "I know that one—"

Enrico suddenly raised his head and screamed, "*You know nothing about me. You have no right—why are you all against me?*"

He wrenched himself out of Karen's arms and backed away a few steps.

"Enrico, please," Karen cried. "Let me get you home."

"*Keep away from me. Leave me alone,*" he screamed. "*Leave me alone!*"

He retreated a few more steps, then turned suddenly and began to run.

"*Leave me alone!*" he screamed over his shoulder.

Helpless, Karen watched him go, uncertain whether to try to follow. But she knew she would never catch up in her high heels, and the man had put a hand, as big and warm as a bear's paw, on her shoulder.

"That one's bad," he said. "Let him go. I have a little *trattoria* just down the street. You come, you sit down, you drink a glass of wine. You feel better."

He propelled her gently along the street until they reached a place where tables stood outside on a small raised island, surrounded by trees hung with coloured lights.

"Now, then," he said, "you sit down, and Papa Vito will bring you a glass of wine."

He pressed Karen into a seat and bustled away. She

regarded him, open-mouthed. Vito. No wonder he looked familiar. Now that she had the time and opportunity to look around her, she realised that she was in the place to which Riccardo had brought her that first night.

For a moment Karen contemplated running away. Then she gave a shrug. It was done now. She would gain nothing by leaving. And besides, she felt too drained of emotion to care. She could no longer feel her own agony, but she had felt Enrico's. His passionate tears had exhausted her.

She was shocked, too, she had to admit. She had been frightened by the desperation of his weeping, the uncontrolled way he had yielded to his emotions.

Why had she defended him so fiercely, she wondered? Because he had clung to her like an abandoned child? And suddenly she heard Riccardo's voice, sneering, "Tell me, Karen, is that what a woman wants—a man who weeps on her shoulder and goes running to her with his misfortunes, like a weakling?"

No, not that. She could never want a man like Enrico, who apparently found it hard to behave like an adult, and who had clung to her because probably he would always cling to the nearest sympathetic woman. But neither did she want a man who was too proud to turn to her for help when he was in pain. And another memory from that night in Milan rose in her mind: Riccardo's face, full of suffering in an unguarded moment, but closed against her even then, shutting her out from his grief because he did not trust her enough to admit to her that he was vulnerable.

She knew now why she had rushed to Enrico's defence. It had touched her heart that he had clung to her, rousing the instinct to protect that was so much a part of her nature. And now she recalled that the moment she had begun to love Riccardo was when she had first seen the almost imperceptible crack in his proud armour.

But what was the use of understanding that now, she thought bitterly? She was shut out from his heart forever, both by his actions and her own. Even if all else could be made right between them—and it was hard to see how that could be—he would never forgive the humiliating insult she had hurled at him in that note. Nor would he forgive her for making a fool of him over the land. From now on his armour would always be in place against her. She had shown too well that she knew how to attack any weak places.

And what kind of heart did he have, anyway, this man who apparently felt so little remorse for his wife's death that he could take his mistress to live in her home? Or had he been glad to be rid of her? He had spoken of being childless. Did he blame his wife for giving him no children? And what did it matter to Karen anyway, since her love for him had died? There was no doubt about that.

"*Buono notte, signorina.* I have brought you your wine. You drink it up quick, *si?*"

Karen had been sitting with her eyes closed, but at the sound of a woman's voice she opened them sharply and stared.

"*Franca!*" she exclaimed. "How did Vito turn into you?"

Franca chuckled in delight and seated herself heavily at Karen's table. A tray bearing a bottle and two glasses lay between them, and she began to pour.

"I am here visiting Vito," she said. "He is a good friend, also his wife Serafina. I am godmother to their youngest child."

"Of course; he used to work for you, didn't he?"

"*Si.* Now I work for him."

"I don't understand."

"When Vito want free help in the kitchen he call me and say, 'Franca, come and eat with us.' We eat together, and then we all wash the dishes." She roared with laughter at her own joke, and Karen smiled.

"Tonight," Franca went on, "Vito tell me you are here. He say you don't look good and you need wine. I say I bring it."

Karen was about to protest that she felt perfectly well when she became aware that something funny was happening to the trees overhead. They seemed to be shifting position, sliding round to the side. The next moment her cheek hit the table, and she was prevented from sliding out of her seat only by Franca's strong hands grasping her shoulder and pulling her back in her chair.

Slowly the trees stopped whirling and settled back into approximately the right position. Franca was holding a glass of wine out to her.

"Drink," she said sternly.

Karen did so, and felt better. She looked apprehensively at Franca, but the old woman had settled back into her own chair and was beaming at her.

"You feel better now," she declared.

"Franca," said Karen, suddenly guilty, "I speak Italian. You don't have to speak English for me."

She said this in Italian, and the old woman laughed again.

"We speak English," she said. "I don't speak Italian that good."

"But, it's your language."

"No. My language is Calabrese. You would say is a dialect, but is different, like a language. When I come to Rome, I have to learn to speak *la madre lingua*. I never learn it too good."

"But you've spoken it all these years."

"Only with some. I manage. But with Alfonso and Riccardo I speak Calabrese."

"Riccardo speaks Calabrese?"

"So. He learn from his papa and from me. Not the others. They don't care. But Riccardo is *my* boy."

She said the last words with simple pride, and it gave Karen a strange feeling to hear Riccardo spoken of as a boy. Riccardo had said Franca still thought of him as seventeen, and it was plainly true.

Franca was pouring out more wine and chuckling.

eccably groomed, but this only accentuated the hag-
dness of his face. He looked as if he hadn't eaten or
t for a week. His eyes seemed to scorch Karen, and she
ed that inwardly he was like a too-tightly coiled spring,
y to lash out at the slightest provocation. Her heart
. Riccardo would make a terrifying enemy, and she
v she had done much to earn his enmity.
f you mean the land—" she began.
do not simply mean your piece of cleverness about
and, Karen; but since you have raised the matter, let
al with it first. That stretch of land was vital to the
as you were well aware. And yet you gave your
r to my brother, knowing how he would use it. You
aused harm for which I will never forgive you. And
r would my father, if he were alive."
n't!" she cried, unable to endure the thought of
o, whom she had unwittingly betrayed. "I never
Gigi to vote against that land deal. I just never
t about it."
condemn yourself with every word you utter," he
dly. "You were so determined to vent your spite
me that you gave not one thought to the
ences. Tell me, Karen, what had I done to deserve
e? Your note to me was a masterpiece of vindic-
What had I done?"
–you went away. . . ." She stopped, realising
ossible it was to explain.
up to answer the phone. That was my crime? But
, I should have been fawning on you like a
wearing eternal love because we had enjoyed a
nent of pleasure together. You place too high a
ourself."
!" she cried, turning away from him with her
r her ears. But he seized her wrists and pulled
.
still much to say to you. You have been too
our own good, Karen. In lashing out at me you

"The signora, she hear us speak our dialect, she get mad."

"I suppose she felt shut out," said Karen.

"*Si.* Then Riccardo, too; that make her really mad. I steal her son, she say. So, when Gigi come, she make him all hers."

"And Riccardo became yours," said Karen impulsively, "as he should have been."

The old eyes twinkled at her. "Ah, Riccardo tell you about that?"

"Yes. He told me the first evening. I . . . wondered how you could bear to live in Alfonso's house."

"Better in his house than out of it," said Franca at once.

"You loved him then?"

"*Si.* All these years." Franca's voice was content and quite devoid of bitterness.

Karen frowned. "And you didn't hate him for what he'd done to you?"

"Signorina," said Franca gently, "a man do what he must, and a woman who loves him must do what he says is right for her."

"That may have been true once," said Karen, "but not now. Not for my generation."

Franca made an impatient gesture. "Your generation, or mine—or which one—it makes no difference. Nothing changes for women. And you have reason to know that, I think."

"I don't know what—" Karen began to protest, but before the kindness in those shrewd old eyes her voice faltered. "I can't be sure yet," she said tiredly.

"I can."

"It's just over a month. No one can be certain so soon," she said helplessly.

But Franca came from a people where a doctor was an unheard of luxury except for the very sick, and at other times women tended each other. She greeted this statement with a derisive snort.

"Dottore do not know for sure. Me, I know. But Riccardo does not, eh?"

Karen shook her head. "I don't know where he is."

"Be back in two days," Franca said firmly. "I know."

"You've always known where he is?"

Franca's eyes became suddenly crafty. "Be back in two days," she repeated, and refused to say more.

"You won't tell him? Promise me you won't."

"Of course," Franca looked shocked. "You must tell. Your business."

Without warning she leaned over and gave Karen a smacking kiss.

"Clever girl." She beamed.

It dawned on Karen that in this fertile country she had now been welcomed into the ranks of the elite, women who were to bear children to their men. The fact that she was an unofficial entry was plainly irrelevant.

"You go home to bed now," Franca ordered. "Get plenty of rest."

Karen couldn't help laughing. "Franca—one month—all right, all right," she ended hastily. "I'll be good. I'll get a taxi."

"Taxi!" Franca was scandalised. "I take you. My car is here."

Franca's car turned out to be a tiny Fiat into which they could both just squeeze. The journey to the hotel was short but full of incident. Franca collided with a fruit barrow, narrowly avoided a cat, and exchanged ritual pleasantries with a driver coming the other way in a narrow street. And Karen, who had thought that Giulietta was the most hair-raising driver she had ever travelled with, discovered she was wrong.

"The signora, she hear us speak our dialect, she get mad."

"I suppose she felt shut out," said Karen.

"*Si.* Then Riccardo, too; that make her really mad. I steal her son, she say. So, when Gigi come, she make him all hers."

"And Riccardo became yours," said Karen impulsively, "as he should have been."

The old eyes twinkled at her. "Ah, Riccardo tell you about that?"

"Yes. He told me the first evening. I . . . wondered how you could bear to live in Alfonso's house."

"Better in his house than out of it," said Franca at once.

"You loved him then?"

"*Si.* All these years." Franca's voice was content and quite devoid of bitterness.

Karen frowned. "And you didn't hate him for what he'd done to you?"

"Signorina," said Franca gently, "a man do what he must, and a woman who loves him must do what he says is right for her."

"That may have been true once," said Karen, "but not now. Not for my generation."

Franca made an impatient gesture. "Your generation, or mine—or which one—it makes no difference. Nothing changes for women. And you have reason to know that, I think."

"I don't know what—" Karen began to protest, but before the kindness in those shrewd old eyes her voice faltered. "I can't be sure yet," she said tiredly.

"I can."

"It's just over a month. No one can be certain so soon," she said helplessly.

But Franca came from a people where a doctor was an unheard of luxury except for the very sick, and at other times women tended each other. She greeted this statement with a derisive snort.

"*Dottore* do not know for sure. Me, I know. But Riccardo does not, eh?"

Karen shook her head. "I don't know where he is."

"Be back in two days," Franca said firmly. "I know."

"You've always known where he is?"

Franca's eyes became suddenly crafty. "Be back in two days," she repeated, and refused to say more.

"You won't tell him? Promise me you won't."

"Of course," Franca looked shocked. "You must tell. Your business."

Without warning she leaned over and gave Karen a smacking kiss.

"Clever girl." She beamed.

It dawned on Karen that in this fertile country she had now been welcomed into the ranks of the elite, women who were to bear children to their men. The fact that she was an unofficial entry was plainly irrelevant.

"You go home to bed now," Franca ordered. "Get plenty of rest."

Karen couldn't help laughing. "Franca—one month—all right, all right," she ended hastily. "I'll be good. I'll get a taxi."

"*Taxi!*" Franca was scandalised. "I take you. My car is here."

Franca's car turned out to be a tiny Fiat into which they could both just squeeze. The journey to the hotel was short but full of incident. Franca collided with a fruit barrow, narrowly avoided a cat, and exchanged ritual pleasantries with a driver coming the other way in a narrow street. And Karen, who had thought that Giulietta was the most hair-raising driver she had ever travelled with, discovered she was wrong.

Chapter Nine

Three days later the phone rang in Karen's apartment. Riccardo's voice spoke abruptly across the line.

"I am waiting for you at the lawyer's office. You'd better come if you don't want to find yourself without a penny left to your name." The line went dead.

Karen stared at the receiver. After four weeks she had finally heard his voice again, a cold harsh voice that spoke to her like a stranger. Her heart had barely finished leaping before he had slammed down the phone.

As soon as she saw him she knew that this was a crisis that dwarfed everything that had gone before. Under the curious eye of the secretary he ushered her courteously into a small anteroom, but as soon as they were alone he turned on her. His face was filled with a black rage, the more alarming for being under icy control. For the first time Karen was afraid of him. He hated her. There was no doubt of it.

"I would not have believed in such malice as yours," he said with soft venom, "unless I had seen it for myself."

He turned away without waiting for an answer and began to pace the room, as though this were the only way he could find release for his tension. As always, he was impeccably groomed, but this only accentuated the haggardness of his face. He looked as if he hadn't eaten or slept for a week. His eyes seemed to scorch Karen, and she sensed that inwardly he was like a too-tightly coiled spring, ready to lash out at the slightest provocation. Her heart sank. Riccardo would make a terrifying enemy, and she knew she had done much to earn his enmity.

"If you mean the land—" she began.

"I do not simply mean your piece of cleverness about the land, Karen; but since you have raised the matter, let us deal with it first. That stretch of land was vital to the firm, as you were well aware. And yet you gave your power to my brother, knowing how he would use it. You have caused harm for which I will never forgive you. And neither would my father, if he were alive."

"Don't!" she cried, unable to endure the thought of Alfonso, whom she had unwittingly betrayed. "I never meant Gigi to vote against that land deal. I just never thought about it."

"You condemn yourself with every word you utter," he said coldly. "You were so determined to vent your spite against me that you gave not one thought to the consequences. Tell me, Karen, what had I done to deserve such hate? Your note to me was a masterpiece of vindictiveness. What had I done?"

"You—you went away. . . ." She stopped, realising how impossible it was to explain.

"I got up to answer the phone. That was my crime? But of course, I should have been fawning on you like a lapdog, swearing eternal love because we had enjoyed a brief moment of pleasure together. You place too high a price on yourself."

"Stop it!" she cried, turning away from him with her hands over her ears. But he seized her wrists and pulled them down.

"I have still much to say to you. You have been too clever for your own good, Karen. In lashing out at me you have also harmed yourself. I could laugh but for the tragedy you have caused."

"I don't understand," she whispered. "What have I done?"

"The papers you signed did not merely give Gigi power to vote your shares. They gave him *full* power. They enabled him to act as though he were you."

"But I never meant that. I just—"

"Did you read what you had signed?"

She hung her head. "No."

He dropped her hands with a gesture of disgust. "You are well served," he said bitterly. "I warned you, did I not, that if you threw in your lot with my brother you would repent. Even I did not imagine that I would be proved right so dreadfully and so soon."

"But what has Gigi *done?*"

"He has been raising money, using your shares as security." As he saw her hands fly to her face and her eyes widen in horror, he added, "I need not ask if any of this money has reached you."

"None of it," she gasped. "I had no idea. How much?"

"It is impossible to judge the exact amount, but I doubt the final figure will be much less than a million pounds."

Karen sank into a chair and buried her head in her hands, overcome with shame. She cared nothing for the money. She knew Alfonso's total bequest to her amounted to far more than a million, but if she had lost every penny she would still have been indifferent. She cared only for the torturing sense that Riccardo despised her and that she had fully deserved his contempt.

After a while she pulled herself together and raised her head.

"I should have thought," she said in a husky voice, "but I never realised that even Gigi could behave like this."

"And yet you had ample evidence, had you not? You saw his losses at the gaming tables?"

"How did you know that?"

He shrugged. "One of the waiters there earns a retainer from me by informing me whenever Gigi goes into the club—also his losses, if he can discover them. The morning after you were there I received a call. This is an unpleasant necessity. I do not enjoy receiving secret information about my brother, but I do it because his losses are a threat to us all."

"But I don't see . . ." She had to stop because she was choking. Not for the world would she let Riccardo witness her tears. "I don't see why he used *my* shares. Why not his own?"

"He doesn't pledge his own because he can't. They're tied up so that he can't raise money against them until he's thirty. My father knew about Gigi's ways and did this to protect him. But the provision does not apply to anyone else. You were a godsend to Gigi."

"But he must have known I'd find out," she said, bewildered.

"Eventually, yes. I think he counted on having rather longer than this. But when payment day came round the creditors would have applied to him in vain. Then they would have come to you. Gigi would have thrown himself on your mercy and used all his 'charm' to persuade you to pay his debts."

"Then I don't see why you say I've damaged the company. It's me Gigi has harmed. No one else."

"You say that because you have not thought. If I had not intervened he would have gone on raising money, so much that perhaps you could not have paid it all back. Then the creditors would have claimed the shares."

"But—surely—you have first option?"

"Yes, and I would have exercised it. But even I could not pay indefinitely. When the year's grace ran out, any shares that I could not afford to buy would fall into the hands of outsiders. There are men who would give anything to own part of my father's firm. Through the weak link of my brother they saw a way of doing so. It would take time, but they are patient. You have assisted them."

She dropped her head back into her hands, overcome by an agony of remorse.

"You waste our time," said Riccardo distantly. "It is too late now for regrets."

Karen forced herself to rise and confront him with her head up. "Is it any use my saying that I'm sorry—asking your forgiveness?" she said in a shaking voice.

He did not answer directly, but after giving her a hard look said, "Do I have your promise that you will do what I say to put matters right?"

"Yes, of course. Is there a way?"

"There is no way to recover the money you have lost. That will have to be paid."

"I'll pay it," she said eagerly.

"No, I will. As your husband it will be my job to do so."

She stared at him, thunderstruck. She had always known that he was prepared to marry her out of necessity, but she had never imagined that the "proposal" would be put in this brutally frank style.

"My husband . . . ?"

"Our marriage is the only thing that will prevent your indulging in this kind of foolishness again. I intend to make myself safe from any further damage you could inflict."

"You can't . . . seriously think of marrying me in this way, for this reason," she stammered.

"Why not?" he said coolly. "The uniting of two properties is an excellent reason for marriage. It has been done since time immemorial. Our children will have much to inherit. And their inheritance will be the greater because I will have prevented you from dissipating it."

"And suppose I want to keep what is my own?" she said hotly.

"Our marriage settlement will arrange for ownership

and control to pass into my hands. I shall have your vote and the income will be paid to me, although naturally I shall hand over a large portion to you. Never fear. My wife will not be kept short of money."

She was about to cry out that she would never marry him in this way, but the words died in her throat. The thought that was never far from her these days killed her passionate rejection. A lead weight fell on her heart. The marriage would go through, and she would die a little inside.

"Very well," she said in a quiet, despairing voice. "I will marry you, Riccardo."

"Good. The marriage settlement will be ready for you to sign in a few moments."

"Marriage settlement?"

"Of course. Wealth such as yours needs special arrangements before the wedding can take place. It must be set out that your property becomes mine for the lifetime of our marriage."

"And how long do you think that is likely to be?" she asked in an ironic voice.

He looked surprised. "I expect our marriage to last until one of us dies, Karen. I beg you, do not be melodramatic over what is a very normal business arrangement. There is no reason why our life together should not be a good one. All I ask of you is children, and a certain level of behaviour appropriate to my wife. If you can comply with these quite normal wishes, you will not find me a tyrannical husband. We shall remain together until death separates us, at which time our property will be differently disposed."

If he said *property* again, she knew she would scream. This was the man she had passionately loved, whose child she might be carrying. And he proposed marriage in the language of the boardroom, speaking of money and power and "a normal business arrangement."

"And suppose your calculations prove inaccurate," she said, trying to match his cool tone, "and our marriage breaks up, after all? What then?"

"In case of divorce or separation, the ownership of your shares returns to you, but power to control them remains with me."

"No," she said at once. "I won't agree to that. If I married you on those terms, you could treat me as you liked, because the one thing you really want would be in your pocket forever. You're the one who wants to regard this solely as a business deal, so now I'm going to be heartless too."

"I have always known you could be heartless, Karen," he said in a soft, deadly voice.

She took a deep breath. "I'll marry you, Riccardo, but on my own conditions. In case of a breakup I get everything back—both ownership and control."

"In other words," he said furiously, "you do not trust me to behave as a decent husband to you. You insult me."

"I propose terms for a merger," she said, fighting to keep her voice steady. "This is a 'normal business arrangement' Riccardo, nothing more. You have said so. Very well. We'll negotiate as we would for any other deal. Starting with the fact that you want this marriage more than I do."

If only he would not guess that she was lying, that she had a reason for wanting this marriage every bit as much as he did. But even in the most dire circumstances she would not accept the kind of settlement he had in mind. Some of Karen's fighting spirit had returned.

For a moment their eyes challenged each other. Then his expression changed to one of grim, ironic humour.

"Why, you are right," he said. "How foolish of me to rely on your honour, on your regard for my father's memory and your remorse for the way you have treated his gift to you."

She faced him bravely. "I never allow a business decision to be affected by sentiment," she said.

They were his own words from that evening in Milan, flung before him now like a gauntlet. As he recognised them, something that might almost have been admiration gleamed in his eyes for a fraction of a second, and was gone.

"Your entire behaviour shows that to be untrue," he said. "But let us argue the point no further. Having no choice, I agree to your terms."

Without another word he was gone, leaving Karen to wonder what was to happen next. She was not long left in doubt. In five minutes he was back.

"I have made arrangements for the change in the settlement," he said. "All the necessary papers will be ready for your signature in a moment."

She gasped. "But does it have to be done so fast? Surely there's time for all this later?"

"There is no time at all. Within a few minutes we are going to leave here, and I want those documents signed before we go."

"But why the urgency?"

"Because we are eloping, Karen," he said in a cool voice.

She could almost have laughed at the barefaced ruthlessness of it. Instead she regarded him with her head on one side.

"Thus giving me no opportunity to change my mind," she said with as much lightness as she could muster.

"You learn quickly. Good girl," he said approvingly.

"Where exactly are we eloping to?"

"A place called Arella. It is a very small town, about three hours' drive to the north of here. For us it will be ideal. Italy is a difficult country for an elopement. Even for a civil wedding we have to give fourteen days' notice to the Town Hall. However, the officials have discretion to shorten this period if they consider that the circumstances warrant it. Since I have a certain amount of—influence— in the area, I can assure you that discretion will be exercised in our favour."

Apparently as an afterthought he added, "Perhaps I should also mention that I caused my official representative in the area to post the notice of our marriage three days ago."

She drew in her breath sharply, hating him. His eyes met hers, daring her to object.

"In fact, you did it as soon as Franca called to tell you I was back in Rome," she said, venturing a shot in the dark. He gave her a small nod, but said nothing. "You took an awful lot for granted, Riccardo. Suppose I don't want to marry in a rushed ceremony in a Town Hall?"

"If you wish for a religious service, I can arrange for our marriage to be blessed by the church when we return."

"If I wish—" she echoed bitterly. "Do my wishes count for anything?"

He took her hand and kissed it with icy lips.

"For my bride," he assured her, "nothing will be too much trouble."

The agony of the next few days was burned into Karen's brain till the last moment of her life. Worst of all was having to pretend to be a dewy-eyed eloping bride when her heart was breaking.

The lawyer had produced the marriage settlement in double-quick time, acting on the orders of what he plainly took to be a passionate and impatient bridegroom. The whole business had brought out a sense of flirtatious gallantry in him, too long repressed by his profession, and when the last paper was signed he produced a bottle of champagne and insisted on toasting them with it.

Then there was the drive back to her apartment to pack a suitcase and collect her passport. She did all this like an automaton. She had made her decision and there was no further need to think. Besides, if she allowed herself to think she might start screaming.

Riccardo drove them to Arella himself. The drive took just over three hours and they travelled in silence. Everything necessary had already been said.

When they reached the town Karen looked round her and understood why Riccardo had been sure of his influence in this place. The hub of Arella had once been a small village. Onto this had been grafted sprawling modern suburbs, all erected in the last few years. On the outskirts stood the five Tornese factories that had transformed this sleepy corner of the world. The atmosphere was one of cheerful prosperity. Karen glanced out of the corner of her eye at the man sitting beside her. He was a king whose most lightly expressed wish would be eagerly obeyed by those who enjoyed the fruits of his patronage.

Their hotel had been booked in advance. It was small and discreet and looked as if it had been recently modernised. At the desk Karen handed over her passport and was given a key.

"The passport can be returned to you in half an hour," said the receptionist.

At the door of her room Riccardo said, "It is getting late. This hotel has an excellent restaurant. I suggest we eat there, and then you should go to bed early. I shall collect you here in half an hour."

When they went downstairs later Karen went straight to the reception desk.

"May I have my passport now, please?" she said.

The receptionist looked bewildered. "But . . . it has been collected."

"I collected it for you, *cara,*" said Riccardo, coming up behind her.

"Then may I have it, please?"

"Later. I'm not carrying it on me now."

He steered her towards the hotel restaurant, which was outside, with tables under the trees.

"Riccardo, I want my passport," she said furiously.

"Your passport stays with me, Karen," he said in a flat voice. "That way I can be sure you will remain here."

"You've no right to do that."

"Nonetheless, I am doing it."

"What do you hope to gain? If I want to leave here, that wouldn't stop me."

"It would prevent you leaving Italy, however. And I do not think you will go without it."

"I have no intention of running away," she said in a biting tone. "But I will not be made a prisoner. You must be quite mad to think you can treat me like this."

"Perhaps you are right," he said after a moment. "These last few weeks I have watched the great empire that my father built with my assistance threatened with damage and destruction, all because of you. I have seen that the thing to which my whole life has been dedicated could become nothing, could fall into the hands of strangers, unless I took steps to prevent it. Now I have taken those steps, and I will carry them through to the bitter end—no matter how bitter that end may be for both of us. Truly, you may say that a madness has descended on me. Perhaps now you will understand that nothing—*nothing at all*—is going to prevent me from protecting what my father created."

She sat in silence. It was useless to fight him. He was as hard and implacable as a rock. She could smash herself to pieces against him, but she could never move him.

For the rest of the meal he maintained an attitude of aloof, impersonal courtesy. He discussed the Tornese factories in the area and said they would spend the next few days inspecting them.

"I thought I was to keep out of the running of the firm?" said Karen.

"You are. But I prefer to keep you in my company. Even the briefest separation would be too much for my, er, ardour."

She caught her breath at the jeering cruelty of his words. After that she forced herself to match his manner, but inwardly she was weeping.

At her door he bid her good night with a chaste peck on the cheek.

"Good night, Karen. Pleasant dreams. Nothing will occur to disturb you tonight."

Nothing did, and she slept soundly, exhausted by the events of the day.

Even with the utmost exertion of Riccardo's influence there were still three more days for them to wait. As she lived through them Karen was forced to admire the strategy with which he kept their relationship in limbo, contriving to rivet her to his side at all times, yet never being alone with her. During the day there were factories to be inspected, and this part she found genuinely interesting. The evenings were taken up with entertaining local officials.

The very first evening they dined with the mayor, who was profuse in his apologies that even for so great a man as Signor Tornese it had not been possible to reduce the waiting time further. The following night was taken up by more dignitaries, whose names Karen lost track of. They all had one thing in common. They were anxious to please Riccardo Tornese.

She passed through these days in a dream, certain that the world and her life had come to a halt. At night she slept alone. Not once did Riccardo approach her, and even that seemed no more than an inevitable part of the Hades in which she was living.

On the last day Riccardo drove her to a large town nearby so that she could buy something in which to be married. Her mind stood aside and watched her behaviour as if she had been someone else. It saw a girl who had run away to be married, spending a day in her bridegroom's company, allowing him to help her choose her wedding clothes, lunching with her, exchanging apparently friendly conversation. It observed the man, how handsome he was, how attentive, how charming, how remote.

That evening they dined alone. Once he pulled open his jacket to get to an inner pocket, and she saw her passport there, tantalisingly near. He laughed as he saw her face.

"Don't try it, Karen. You would find the results very undignified. Come, don't quarrel with me tonight. It is the night before our wedding. We should be of one accord."

He laid a hand on her arm as he spoke, and she closed her eyes. Against her will her body was subtly yielding to the memories evoked by those slim brown fingers whose touch on her bare flesh was so deceptively light, yet so implicitly powerful.

The past month faded away as though it had never been. It was only yesterday that those hands had held her to him with such gentle strength, knowing how and where to touch her intimately so that she melted with desire. Her body had not forgotten those caresses. It ached for them still, making a mockery of her mind's rejection. Her hostility faded, and she was left with a yearning for the joy she had known, and which had so soon been poisoned.

Poison: Riccardo had called it the Italian weapon, the subtle murderer that kills from within. She had thought he was joking.

She heard a sound like an intake of breath and looked up to find Riccardo's burning eyes fixed on her. For a moment she thought she had surprised a moment's pain in them, but it was so fleeting that she might have imagined it.

"Yes," he said simply. "I too have remembered what once nearly lay between us."

"*Nearly.*" She echoed the word with whispered longing.

That night, before going to bed, she threw open her French windows and stood looking out over the city. With her whole body she was conscious of Riccardo just on the other side of the wall.

She went out onto her balcony and stood feeling the cool air play over her body through the thin silk of her nightdress. Her eyes were drawn as by a magnet to the adjoining balcony of Riccardo's room. His French windows stood wide open, and she could see a faint light within his room. Close by the window stood a chair with his jacket thrown over the back. What a pleasure it would be to take her passport from him without his knowledge. If only she could be sure of escaping undetected.

The sound of noisily running water coming from the bathroom told her that he was in the shower. In a moment she was over the low wall that separated their balconies, and in through the window. It took a second for her to run her hands through the jacket.

The passport wasn't there. Dismayed, she went through the pockets again, so intent on her search that she did not hear the sudden silence from the bathroom, and knew nothing until a hand came down and grasped her wrist, jerking her to her feet.

"How foolish of you to think you could catch me out," said Riccardo mildly.

She tried to pull away, furious at being discovered like this, but he kept hold of her wrist. He was naked except for a small towel about his loins. His body glistened with water so that every contour was accentuated, and he seemed to tower over her in the semidarkness.

"You are not to be trusted with anything, are you?" he went on in a hard voice. "Tonight I indulged in a moment of foolish sentimentality, and you assumed I was lowering my guard. But I shall never lower my guard against you, Karen. You are too skilled at discovering my weak places, and using them against me."

"I had a perfect right to recover my own property," she flashed.

"And I have the right to protect myself against you. I intend to—always."

"But we can't live like that," she cried passionately.

"Why not? We won't be the only married couple to live in a state of armed truce."

At the bleakness in his voice something inside her snapped. For three days she had been fighting down a rising tide of hysteria, but now her calm shattered. She was past caring what she said or did.

"I won't do it!" she screamed. *"I won't marry you like this—you're not human—"*

The words were choked off as she was pulled hard against his chest and held there by arms of steel. Her tears would not be repressed. They poured down her cheeks as despair shook her. Riccardo's hand was in her hair, pressing her face against his shoulder, while his deep voice murmured soothingly in her ear.

"Hush, *carina,* hush. Come, now, do not make a tragedy. It will not be so terrible, I promise you. We shall learn to live together. No," he said as she tried to pull away, holding her fast, "if you must weep, let it be in my arms. I am to be your husband. Who else should comfort you but myself?"

They were the first affectionate words he had spoken to her since the night in Milan, and they caused her tears to flow faster with the anguish of loss. She felt her head pulled gently backwards so that her face was raised to his, naked and defenceless. What he saw there made him catch his breath sharply, and he began to kiss her wet cheeks. Then his mouth was on hers, and she could taste her own tears on his lips. His unexpected tenderness destroyed the last of her strength, and she clung to him. His lips brushed her face with feather-light movements, still murmuring words of comfort that she could no longer distinguish. She gave herself up to the sweet ache that pervaded her at his touch and slid her arms round him, drawing him as close to her as she could. She began to caress his back, thrilling at the smooth ripple of muscles under the wet gleaming skin. Their enmity was unimportant. It belonged to another world. This was the only world that mattered, where they could cast away anger and meet in the consuming passion that alone united them.

She sensed him trying to draw away as though confused by the change he found in her, but she put out all her strength to draw his head down, offering him her mouth, open and inviting. When he seized it she bravely took the attack into his territory, flickering her tongue lightly round the inside of his mouth, feeling his vibrant response through her skin, knowing that her teasing was driving him to the point of insanity. With a feverish hand she traced the length of his spine and felt the convulsive movement he made against her, knew that the urgency of his desire was destroying the defences he had built against her.

She drew him down onto the bed, luring him on with the demands of her lips, her tongue, her hands. She discovered that she knew about love, knew by instinct all the little ways to incite a man to greater passion and tantalise him till he reached the explosion point. How she came by the knowledge she couldn't tell. It was as old as time, born into every woman, only waiting discovery at the right time. With her it had waited till this one man had called it irresistibly forth.

It was she who was making love to him, she whose hands tugged at the towel, freeing his loins for what she urgently demanded of them. Her whole body cried aloud for the fulfilment only he could give her. She thought her moment had come, and called his name. But something was wrong. He had stiffened against her and was thrusting her from him. She looked up and saw his face rigid with shock.

"I thought I knew all your tricks," he grated. "But you had one left that I never dreamed of—tears, cynically used to show me how easily you could pierce my defences at the very moment I was boasting of them. A really clever woman would have waited, instead of flaunting her power in my face at once."

"I didn't—" she stammered. "Riccardo, please—"

"It wasn't enough for you that I should desire you," he raged. "You had to show me that you could *make* me desire you. I was to dance to your tune, wasn't I?"

He jerked her up off the bed, holding her cruelly against him. "And you are very seductive, Karen, I will not deny that. Almost you succeeded. Where did you learn your tricks to inflame a man's passion, I wonder? How do you know how to use your allure as a weapon to sap his strength and make him in thrall to you? That's what you'd like to do with me, isn't it?"

"And if I were fool enough to yield? Would there be another nasty little note, a new way of insulting me? Oh, no. You managed to humiliate me once before; you'll not be allowed to succeed again."

As he led her to the window she feared her legs would give way beneath her.

"You had better go this way," he said curtly. "And we shall forget that tonight ever happened."

She wrenched herself out of his grasp and managed to steady herself long enough to climb over the dividing wall. Once inside her own room she locked the windows before falling onto her bed to sob out her misery.

The following day she watched her own wedding as if in a dream. This was the man in whose arms she had once lain, delirious with passionate love. Yet their lives were united in a chilly, impersonal ceremony lasting a bare ten minutes. Afterwards he drove her straight to the airport.

"How are you going to tell your family?" she asked him on the flight home.

"The family already know. I called them from Arella. You will find Franca all over you. She is delighted. She said she was glad I had learned some sense."

"And that was all?"

"After that my mother seized the phone from her."

Karen breathed a silent prayer, uncertain whether she had been reprieved or not. Franca would be bound to think that Riccardo knew about the possible baby, and that this was the reason for the hasty wedding. It would have been natural for her to blurt this out. Yet she seemed to have said nothing—unless she had spoken to the signora when the call was over.

Common sense told Karen that her wisest course was to tell Riccardo about the baby. Yet she could not bear to. The moments that should have been precious to him—his proposal, their wedding—these had been ruined by the way it had all happened. The moment when she told him she was to have his child must somehow be saved. She would wait until the atmosphere between them improved —if only Franca had held her tongue.

In Rome they drove straight to her apartment. Riccardo left again at once, saying he would return soon. Karen stretched out wearily on a chair. She supposed Riccardo had gone downstairs to see if he could find Gigi. There must be much that the two brothers would have to say to each other.

But he returned within ten minutes, frowning. He made two phone calls, one to his mother, the other to the office.

"Nobody has seen Gigi since the day before yesterday," he said when he had replaced the receiver. "He hasn't been at work, and he isn't at home. He must have gone to earth. It was to be expected. I called him also from Arella and told him that his little game was over. It matters not at all. He will turn up eventually.

"My mother wishes us to go to her for dinner tonight. I should like to please her in this, but I shall not insist if you are tired."

Nothing could have been more courteous than his manner of deferring to her, but his voice was completely devoid of warmth, and Karen realised with a sinking heart that he had set a barrier of cool propriety between them that would be harder for her to cope with than his anger.

Before she could answer the telephone rang. When she answered it Giulietta's voice, gasping and tearful, came across the line.

"Something terrible has happened, Karen. Is Maria. We don't know where she is. She was away last night—with a friend she say—but I call the friend. Maria did not go—Karen, are you there?"

"Yes, I'm here," said Karen mechanically. A cold hand had clutched at her stomach. She knew what had happened.

"Is Gigi there?" Giulietta wailed. "Have you seen him?"

"No. Riccardo's been trying to find him. No one knows where he is either."

Giulietta gave a little scream and burst into violent sobbing. When Karen had put the phone down she turned to Riccardo.

"What exactly did you say to Gigi when you called him from Arella?"

"That I knew what he had been doing and intended to put a stop to it. I told him you had withdrawn his power to act for you, and that you and I were to be married."

"How did he take it?"

"Remarkably coolly. He just said 'Oh, well, in that case . . .' Why do you ask?"

"I think he's run off with Maria. She's been missing about the same length of time he has. And that poor girl is in love with him. I suppose her dowry would be considerable?"

"It would be very large. Also, she has her mother's fortune. Dear God, what are we saying? I refuse to believe such a thing. Even Gigi would not seduce a schoolgirl."

But she saw from his white face that he did believe it. Perversely she began to argue the other side of the case, to comfort him.

"We may be jumping to conclusions," she said. "Gigi would have to persuade Pietro to let them marry before he could get his hands on the money. He must have considered that—"

"Persuade?" Riccardo laughed harshly. "Pietro will be on his knees begging Gigi to make an honest woman of his daughter."

He seized the telephone and called Giulietta. After a terse conversation he replaced the receiver.

"For the moment they are keeping calm in case it should be a false alarm," he said. "The first need is for us all to talk together. They will be at my mother's house tonight. But for the moment nothing is to be said. I do not wish my mother worried. Gigi is away on business, and Maria is visiting friends. That is all she needs to be told."

That evening at the villa was one of the strangest of Karen's life. Beneath the surface of a happy family party, currents seethed and whirled. There was scarcely one person there, Karen reflected, who at some point was not involved in an urgent whispered conversation. Only the signora seemed oblivious, presiding over the festivities as though it were an ordinary wedding party.

Karen's first priority was to seize Franca and take her aside.

"Clever girl," said Franca at once.

"Franca, have you said anything?"

The old head shook in vigorous denial.

"Bless you. I . . . haven't told him yet. I'm waiting for the right moment."

"Clever girl," said Franca again. "My Rik marry you for love. This way he don't feel he had to. That's good."

Karen realised that the true explanation for their marriage would never have occurred to simple, honest Franca. To Franca there was love and there were babies, either together or separately. Anything else was just meaningless talk. With all her heart Karen hoped Franca would never know the truth. Franca was one person whose good opinion she desperately wanted to keep.

Giulietta was faring badly. Her face was white and

strained. Pietro tried to calm her, but he was plainly puzzled at her exaggerated grief over a step-daughter she had never liked.

"Don't forget, Gigi is her brother," Karen told him. "If he has really done this thing, she is bound to feel badly."

"True," Pietro scowled. "The shame of such behaviour touches the whole family. I will kill my daughter before I permit her to marry such a one."

"But, if she doesn't marry him—"

"Her good name is gone. And so everyone thinks I must allow this marriage. Doubtless Gigi also thinks so. But do you imagine I shall allow my daughter to tie herself for life to one like that? Better she be disgraced and single than married to a man who disgraces her."

He returned to his wife, leaving Karen open-mouthed at this unexpected common sense.

The evening ended early. Riccardo explained that Karen was tired after the flight. It was only when they were in the car that she realised she had no idea where they were going. After a few moments it became clear that they were heading back to Rome.

"Are we going to stay in a hotel?" she asked.

"My dear Karen, whatever for? The apartment will be enough for the moment. I didn't imagine that you wanted to stay in my mother's house."

"No, but—that is, I hadn't thought about where we were going to live."

"Of course not. Tomorrow you can start looking for a house for us. It can be wherever you like—in the country, in the city. That is your decision."

When they had closed their own front door he set down the suitcase that Franca had packed for him and said, "The sooner you find us a house the better. I don't wish to clutter this small apartment with too many of my things in addition to yours."

"But you have a house, haven't you Riccardo?" she said suddenly. "A villa in the hills."

"Who told you that?" he said in a sharp voice.

"Giulietta, the day I arrived. She said you divided your time between your mother's home and your own. I thought a villa in the hills sounded rather nice." Some little demon was driving her on.

There was a moment's silence before he replied, "If you wish to live in a country villa, then by all means look for one."

"But why should I, when you have one already. Why can't we live there?"

"Because I do not choose to," he said briefly.

"I thought the home was my decision."

"It is. And I have already told you that I will live in the town or the country, as you wish. But I will not take you to the house where I lived with my first wife, and I hope you will now have the good taste to drop this subject, Karen."

She should have left it there, but the demon would not let her alone.

"You'll be selling it then?" she persisted.

"That is for me to say. I have asked you to drop this subject."

"Why should you keep it now?"

He turned on her a look of such hatred that she took a step backwards. When she could take no more of that burning gaze she ran into the bedroom. She slammed the door and sank onto the bed, her head in her hands. It was all true, everything Gigi had told her about Alicia. Riccardo kept his mistress in the villa and intended to continue the arrangement.

It didn't matter, she told herself fiercely. Whatever Riccardo might imagine, this marriage would not last. She would stay with him long enough to give his child his name; then she would go, taking her inheritance with her. It was for this reason that she had fought him about the marriage settlement.

She undressed and slipped on her nightdress, but she did

not want to go to bed. Her mind was wakeful and restless. This was her wedding night, and she felt lost and alone.

With a jolt of horror she realised the real implications of living here. This was where Riccardo had brought the women he had picked up for a night or two. He had lain with them in this very bed. Any moment now he would come to her and claim his rights as her husband—here, where he had enjoyed so many hours with light women.

No. Her mind shouted the word so loudly that she thought she must have spoken it. She would die before she would let this happen. In a moment she was at the door, but she was too late. As her fingers reached out to turn the key, the door swung open and Riccardo stood before her. His ironic glance fell on her outstretched hand, and she saw that he had divined her intent.

"You weren't thinking of locking me out, were you, Karen?" he said slowly. "Such behaviour would hardly become a bride on her wedding night."

She backed away as he came further into the room and shut the door behind him. He was wearing only a red silk dressing gown, loosely tied at the waist.

"Riccardo, please, we're not an ordinary bride and groom. With us there are special reasons. I'd like to think before we—"

"There is nothing to think about," he grated. "There are no 'special reasons' for you to refuse me what is mine by right."

There was hostility in his gaze and determination not to yield an inch. With despair she remembered that Riccardo had an insult to avenge. He hated her for what she had done to him that night in Milan.

"Riccardo, I know I'm your wife, but—"

"There is no *but*—"

She put out a hand to ward him off. "Keep away from me," she cried. "You won't touch me while we're here. I mean it."

She regretted the words the moment she saw the glint that appeared in Riccardo's eyes.

"I see you understand the significance of this place," he said. "From Gigi, I suppose?"

"All right," she yelled at him. "I know you used this place for your women. And I'm not going to be one of them."

Before she knew it his hand had encircled her waist and his fingers had flattened against the small of her back. She could feel their heat through the thin material of her nightdress. Slowly, inexorably, he drew her closer to him until his lips were very near her face. She felt his breath hot against her skin. His voice was grim.

"You are no frightened little virgin. I have reason to know that. You have known passion in my arms before. And you were eager enough last night, when you thought you could make a fool of me."

He smothered her mouth with his own. She gasped as his tongue invaded, rasping against her soft flesh, eliciting a response she could not hide. The flimsy nightdress tore in his hands as though it had been a cobweb. Then he had discarded his dressing gown and was holding her possessively against his naked body. His hands roved intimately over her.

"You knew how it would be when you married me. You told me I could not force you. You married me for reasons of your own, Karen. I wonder what they were."

His hand had intertwined in her hair in what was almost a caress. She could not move her head as he stared down at her, trying to read her face. She had no choice but to meet his piercing gaze.

"What did you want from me, Karen?" he murmured huskily.

He released her hair and his fingers began to trace the outline of her breast. She moaned as he rasped his hand across the nipple, sending flames raging through her. Then he cupped the swell in his palm, caressing it gently until the flood of ecstasy threatened to deprive her of her senses.

When he laid her on the bed she tried again to push him away, but her arms were weak. In a moment he lay beside her. She closed her eyes to shut him out, but it made no difference. His hands were always there, flooding her with heat wherever they touched. The fingers gently stroked the satiny skin of her inner thigh before moving towards the dark moist warmth. She clutched him to her, lost to everything but her desperate need for fulfillment.

Deep down a throbbing ache had started, an ache that pulsed stronger and stronger until it took control of her. She wrapped her legs about his powerful frame until she could feel the violence of his desire against her. Her fingers clutched at his hair so tightly that she heard him gasp with pain. Then his body was pressing her downwards, and he took possession of her with fierce arrogance. She thought she cried for mercy, but the sound became confused with his voice calling her name, over and over.

She woke a little while later to find him asleep with his head between her breasts. Strangest of all, her arms had curved round his head and shoulders in an attitude of protection. She lay still for a long while, staring into the darkness and holding him.

Chapter Ten

It was pure chance that the lift in the apartment block happened to break down one afternoon when Karen was returning from a shopping trip. Otherwise she would not have had to walk up to the fourth floor and past Gigi's apartment.

"Enrico," she said, astonished. "What are you doing here?"

The boy turned from ringing Gigi's bell, and beamed at her. "*Signorina,* I did not know that you lived here, so close to my friend."

"You're a friend of Gigi's?"

"Of course. It was he introduced me to—but that is no matter. You know him?"

"He's my brother-in-law. I married his brother Riccardo three weeks ago."

She barely heard his flood of polite congratulations. Her mind was working.

"Come up and have coffee with me," she said. "We can't talk here."

In the apartment she made coffee and served it to him. He looked haggard and ill.

"Please," he said anxiously, "you can tell me where Gigi is?"

"I'd tell you if I knew, Enrico, but none of us know. You obviously haven't been in touch with Giulietta?"

He looked at her proudly. "I am an honourable man, signora. Giulietta says she no more wishes to see me. Pouf! I cease to exist."

There was something touching in the pathetic dignity of these words. Despite his behaviour at their last meeting she found herself respecting the young man.

He flushed before going on. "I find I must apologise to you for the things I said when we last met."

"Please," she said hastily. "It's of no importance. Let us say no more. I only mentioned Giulietta because if you'd talked to her you'd have known about Gigi's disappearance. He's run away with Maria, and no one knows where they are."

"Infamia!" His reaction was instantaneous. "She is a child."

"That's how we all feel. You were his friend. Perhaps—would you be able to imagine where he could have taken her, from your knowledge of him?"

He ran his hands through his hair. "If I knew I would tell you. That pig-of-pigs has taken my money."

Karen groaned. "You also. Was it much?"

"It was more than I ever expect to have in my hands again. I last saw Gigi three weeks ago, at a gaming club. He was in a dreadful state, very wild. He kept saying 'I am going to put my neck in the hangman's noose.' He lost much money. But I won ten million lire. That would be perhaps five thousand English pounds. And Gigi asked me to lend him this money, and he would pay me back soon. He is my friend. I trust him. But since then I cannot contact him."

It didn't surprise Karen to discover that Gigi had made a friend of someone so very much poorer than himself.

Doubtless Enrico had been dazzled by Gigi's wealth and glamour. Gigi would like that.

"Have you thought of Venice?" said Enrico suddenly.

"Venice? No. You think they might be there?"

"Gigi has a friend who owns an old ruined *palazzo* on one of the smaller islands. I have heard him speak of it as a place of refuge."

"Enrico, you may have done us a service," she said excitedly. "Will you let me repay you the money Gigi owes? The Tornese family should do that for you."

"Grazie, signora," he said in a sad voice. "How I should like to be proud and refuse. As it is . . ."

At once Karen reached for her chequebook. As she was handing the cheque over the door opened and Riccardo entered. His eyes narrowed as he saw Enrico. Karen realised that he probably knew the boy as a friend of Gigi's and disapproved of him.

"Enrico has told me something that may be helpful in finding Gigi," she said quickly. "He's spoken of a place in Venice—"

Enrico had risen to his feet and flushed under the look in Riccardo's eyes. But he kept his dignity as he repeated what he had told Karen.

"How fortunate for us that you should be willing to betray my brother," said Riccardo coldly. "I am unable to think of a single reason why you should do so. Just as I am unable to think why my wife should be paying you money."

"That's wickedly unjust," Karen protested hotly. "You know Gigi well enough to realise they'd be one and the same reason."

"My brother owes you money, signore?"

"Si. Ten million lire that he borrowed from me after I had won it gambling."

"Ah, yes, I had heard. In that case the money must be

returned to you, but not by my wife. Kindly hand that cheque back, and I will replace it."

Enrico obeyed at once, looking miserable. When Riccardo had finished scribbling a cheque he handed it over with a slight gesture to the boy to leave. Enrico's eyes met Karen's in agonised appeal.

"Signora, if you should see—"

"Yes," she said. "I will. Good-bye, Enrico."

When the door had closed behind him Karen looked up to find her husband giving her a long, hard look.

"I thought Vito was mistaken," he said at last. "He told me that he had seen that—thing—in your arms. I did not believe him."

"He was unhappy—drunk—that night. I was trying to help him. That was all."

"So I might have believed if I had not returned home today to find him here, alone with you. And you were handing him money."

"I told you why. Gigi owed it to him. You said you knew about it. I suppose your spy at the club informed you."

"Luckily for you he did. I do not believe the worst of you, Karen, because it would degrade me to do so. And strange as it may seem I trust you. In matters such as these I believe you to be completely trustworthy." He took a step closer and lifted her chin in his hand. His touch was curiously gentle. "No, you would not deceive me."

She looked him in the eyes, too angry to care what she said.

"I decline to feel flattered at that, because it's only your massive conceit that makes you say it. The fact is that I could deceive you right under your nose again and again and you wouldn't see a thing because you couldn't face the fact that any woman could prefer another man to you."

Reckless, dangerous as she knew the words to be, she couldn't wish them unsaid when she saw how his face whitened round the mouth, and knew that she had struck home. But there was no explosion of temper. Instead he said in a quiet voice, "For both our sakes, let us hope the day never comes when our marriage depends on my taking your unsupported word. Because on such an occasion I would remember what you have just said." Abruptly he dropped her chin and turned away. "There is still something about Enrico Perioni that you have not told me. But that can wait. I am home early because we are to go to the opera. Have you forgotten?"

Enrico's visit had driven everything out of her head. Tonight was the opening of the autumn season of the Rome Opera, and they would have to be there. It was a chance for Roman society to catch a glimpse of Riccardo Tornese's new bride, about whom there had been so much speculation following their romantic runaway marriage. And for the bride herself it was a chance to show off her groom's wedding present of sapphires and diamonds, the best that Bonnicelli's had to offer.

The Bonnicellis themselves would be present, stifling their anxiety over their missing daughter. Not that Maria was exactly missing. She had several times telephoned to tell her father that she was safe. But she declined to say where she was, or to return, until she had permission to marry Gigi.

When Karen was ready she looked at herself critically and could find no fault. The heavy white silk dress fell magnificently against her slender body. She had ordered it from one of Rome's top fashion houses to set off the diamonds and sapphires. She touched them where they gleamed at her throat and sighed a little. There was nothing personal in the gift. It had been chosen for its appropriateness for Riccardo Tornese's wife. It had no meaning for Karen Conway.

They dined at Rome's most fashionable restaurant. Under any other circumstances Karen would have had a wonderful time. She knew that she was beautiful and that her husband thought so. There was a hot look in his eyes whenever they fell on her that ought to have thrilled her, but did not, because it was accompanied by a kind of wry wariness that reminded her they were still enemies. As though she could ever forget it. Even at their moments of deepest passion Riccardo never laid aside his defences.

There was a constant stream of visitors to their table. The pretexts varied but the true reason was always the same. Karen knew she was being studied and did her best to be a credit to her husband, but the effort made her nervous.

"Don't try so hard," he said during one of their rare moments alone. "There is no need. You are very much admired by my friends. I am proud of you."

He spoke without warmth, and she hardly knew how to reply. In a moment another visitor joined them.

Giulietta and Pietro were late, joining the Torneses at the theatre just ten minutes before the curtain went up. They had plainly quarrelled, and Giulietta looked as though she had been crying. She beckoned to Karen to come out into the corridor behind the boxes.

"Maria rang me again last night," she declared. "She threaten me again. Either I persuade Pietro to agree to this marriage or—" she gave a helpless shrug. "So I try. Today I plead and argue with him. All day we fight. He say no. He say, A girl with her money, the men line up to marry her, never mind what she's done."

"I saw Enrico today," said Karen in a low voice.

"Oh, Karen, how was he?" Giulietta's eyes had filled with tears.

"He didn't look too well. But he said he had no intention of bothering you again. And I *think* he wants me to tell you that he still loves you, but Riccardo came in before he could say it, so the message was a bit incomplete."

"Did Riccardo ask why he was there?" said Giulietta, her eyes wide with alarm.

"It's all right. Enrico wanted some money Gigi owed him, so he went to Gigi's apartment, which is just under ours. I invited him upstairs. Riccardo wasn't too pleased, but I managed to pass it off."

"Then Riccardo knows nothing? Oh, Karen, I beg of you—"

"It's all right, Giulietta. I promise." Karen noticed with some asperity that Giulietta had no thought for Enrico's plight, or the trouble Karen might find herself in. Her concern was all for her own difficulties.

"Enrico mentioned a place on one of the Venetian islands where he thought they might be," she went on. "I expect Riccardo is telling Pietro about it now."

"Then I am lost," Giulietta murmured. "Pietro will find them. Maria will tell him everything about me." She raised her eyes suddenly. "Oh, Karen, you are so lucky to be married to my darling Rikki. He is a man who would know how to treat a woman."

"Did his first wife tell you that?" said Karen with an irony she could not suppress.

"I did not know her," said Giulietta hurriedly. "I was only a child when it all happened."

"I understood she died only two years ago. You weren't a child then."

"I did not mean her death. I meant . . . everything else." She was searching Karen's face fearfully. Suddenly her eyes brightened with relief. "There is the bell for the start of the performance. Let us go in."

Karen watched the stage, barely aware of what she was seeing. Giulietta had said 'everything else,' which meant there was some secret about Riccardo's marriage other than the manner of his wife's death. Of course she might simply be referring to Alicia, but Giulietta had seemed to imply some specific incident, rather than a drawn-out situation.

And what about her other words: "You are so lucky to be married to my darling Rikki." Giulietta's view was presumably shared by all the women who had given Karen curious and envious looks that evening.

What would they say, she wondered, if I could speak aloud and tell them the truth about my marriage? Suppose I told them that my husband tortures me with passion every night, taking me to dizzying heights that almost deprive me of my sanity, until I tremble in his arms from the force of my own fulfilled desire. No woman was ever possessed with such intensity, but it gives me no joy, because inside himself he remains aloof.

His own pleasure is something that he takes from me, not something that I give. Never does he allow me to feel I have anything to give him, for then he would have to ask of me. And he is too proud—and too much my enemy—to ask me for anything.

But I could also tell of the other times, when his strength has conquered me totally, and I am reduced to weeping the tears of despair. Then he cradles me against his chest as gently as any woman could want and whispers words of tenderness and comfort—but never of love—until I am lulled to sleep in his arms.

In the morning I am always alone. I never wake to find his face sleepy and vulnerable on the pillow beside me. And when I next see him he is once again the aloof, courteous stranger that I know during the day. It is as though my lover of the night had never existed.

I don't ask about the nights he spends away from me, because in my heart I know the answer. I wonder what he has told Alicia about his marriage. I lie alone on those nights, tossing and turning, picturing them together, talking about me. Or perhaps not talking at all. Imagining that is the worst misery.

So I endure my torment, and the world thinks I am a happy bride. Time passes, and I wonder how much longer I can keep my secret. While Riccardo maintains his barricades in place against me I cannot tell him that I am carrying his child. I am in a trap, and I can see no way out.

It was during the second interval, when they were strolling in the corridor, that Riccardo said to Karen, "I shall have to leave you alone for a few days. Pietro wishes me to accompany him to Venice."

"You're sure they'll be there?"

"It seems possible. Pietro says Maria's mother came from Venice, and she has always longed to see the place. They were going to make a sentimental trip there together the year he married my sister. Instead he took Giulietta to Venice for their honeymoon. Maria has never forgiven him."

"I don't blame her," said Karen hotly.

To her surprise Riccardo replied, "I agree with you. He seems to have treated his daughter with a lack of sensitivity that does much to explain her behaviour. I think we'll find them there. We fly to Venice tomorrow. I don't know how long it may take to locate this island. There are many in the lagoon."

"Are you going to pilot yourself?"

"Yes, I think so."

"You will be careful?" she said involuntarily.

He gave her a small bow. "I appreciate your wifely concern, Karen, but I can assure you it is quite misplaced."

She flushed, but recovered, and spoke with a creditable imitation of his own ironic tone.

"I wouldn't exactly call it concern. The fact is, I barely had time to read the marriage settlement before I signed it, so I can't be certain that you've left me enough to make me a merry widow."

His eyes flashed appreciation, as they often did when she came back at him, she realised. Whatever he might say, Riccardo enjoyed the fact that she had the wit to engage him in the odd verbal skirmish.

"You would, of course, recover your own property. That alone would be enough to make you a very merry widow indeed. There would also be the income from mine until such time as any children of our marriage grew to maturity." He hesitated. "It is of course far too soon to know if there is any possibility—"

"Need we discuss that now?" she said uncomfortably.

"You are right. The time is not appropriate. Well, now that I have set your mind at rest about my provision for your future—"

"I no longer have any cause to worry. I shall even be glad to be rid of you for a few days," she managed to say lightly.

"I am delighted to hear it. You make it easier for me to tell you that I shall not be coming home with you tonight. I have things to do elsewhere."

She wanted to scream, "You're going to spend the night with her." But something held her back. His face was closed against her. His eyes warned her to ask no questions. She turned away, biting her lip.

At the end of the evening he drove her to the door of the apartment block and escorted her up the steps. There he stopped.

"Aren't you even coming up to pack a bag?" She tried to keep the pleading out of her voice.

"That will not be necessary. Good-bye, Karen." He gave her a cold kiss on the cheek, and was gone.

For the next few days she occupied herself in house-hunting. From time to time she called Giulietta, but after several phone calls and messages failed to find her, Karen began to wonder if her sister-in-law was avoiding her.

Each night was worse than the one before, an agony of yearning and jealousy and despair. Sometimes she thought she would fly back to England before Riccardo returned. But even if she could have borne to leave him, she still did not have her passport.

One night, unable to sleep, she got up and wandered out into the living room. In one corner stood a large desk which Riccardo kept locked. The urge to look inside it was overwhelming. After a moment Karen ceased to fight it. She got a small knife from the kitchen and forced the lock.

She found what she was looking for in the very first drawer. But the wood was slightly warped, and she couldn't open it more than a couple of inches. She could see the passport but not reach it. She gave the drawer a tug, which made it shoot out suddenly, spilling its contents over the floor.

She piled everything back. Last to go in was a letter which she tossed on the top. It was addressed to Sgnr. Tornese Riccardo, Villa Terranova, Monte d'Este, Roma.

So there it was, the address of Riccardo's villa—the place where he kept Alicia. By an evil chance she could pinpoint Monte d'Este exactly. She had seen it signposted the day she arrived in Rome. She could get there easily. Drive along the Appian Way and then swing north just where . . .

She shut off the thought. What fantastic dreams was she dreaming? The villa was out of bounds to her forever.

The next day she bought herself a car to help with the house-hunting. In the days that followed she went through the motions of living a normal life. She called Giulietta several times without result. In the evenings she talked to Riccardo on the phone in a voice that astonished her by its steadiness. He expected his stay in Venice to be prolonged. The search was going badly, and when it ended there might be further delays at the airport. The air traffic controllers were threatening to strike.

She had lunch with her mother-in-law. She went to the opera. She went on shopping expeditions. All the time the address seemed to burn a hole in her brain.

After four days of feverish activity and four nights without sleep, she finally gave in. She had no idea what she was going to do or say when she reached the villa. She only knew she couldn't stay away any longer.

It was late afternoon as she drove along the Appian Way, and a mellow sun flooded the old stones with golden light. She turned off onto a smaller road and felt herself climbing. She could see Monte d'Este long before she came to it, clinging to the side of a hill, so that from below it presented a forest of red roofs.

At the farthest end of the village she asked directions and was told that the Villa Terranova was three kilometres further on. Ten minutes driving brought her to the place. She was nervous. The big wrought-iron gates had a forbidding look, even though they stood open and no one tried to prevent her entry. Any minute now she might come across Alicia—and then what? What would she say to the woman Riccardo loved?

The grounds were huge. It was like driving through a wonderland. Birds called each other softly from the palm trees. All around was beauty, lovingly tended. Everywhere flowers were massed, white magnolia, red-and-white oleander, pink-and-mauve azaleas. What sort of woman spent her days in this enclosed fairy-tale place, waiting for the man she loved?

Suddenly the road curved, and Karen found herself in front of the villa. Its yellow stone glowed in the warm light, and flowers grew round the steps that led up to the open front door. But what held Karen thunderstruck was the sight of Franca's little car in the drive.

Franca. The last person she would have expected to be connected with Riccardo's other life—or even to know about it. Franca, whom she had foolishly thought was on her side.

As she mounted the steps a small dark man rushed out of the front door and placed himself squarely in her path.

"You don't come in," he said. "No one comes in if I don't know them."

"I am the Signora Tornese," said Karen with as much assurance as she could muster. "Let me pass, please."

For a moment the man seemed taken aback. Then he planted himself more firmly. "I have no orders about you," he said.

Then a familiar voice came from behind him. "Don't make a fool of yourself, Mario. Let the signora come in."

Franca bustled forward and shouldered the man unceremoniously aside. Her face beamed with pleasure at the sight of Karen.

"I have no orders," the man repeated defensively.

"You have orders now," Franca yelled at him. "*I* am giving you the orders, and if you disobey them it will be the worse for you. This is the master's wife. Now get into the kitchen and tell the cook we want a pot of English tea. Move quickly."

Mario was already scuttling away. The two women looked at each other.

"So you have come at last," said Franca.

Karen nodded. "I have to see Alicia for myself. But I've only just discovered where she is. Riccardo doesn't know—"

"*Si.* Many times I have told him that he ought to tell you everything, but he will not. You must understand him—he is afraid—but I know always that if you love him you will find your way here in the end."

"I do love him," said Karen sadly. "But I can't live like this anymore. I won't be put off. I must meet Alicia. I must know what to think."

Franca nodded. "It's time," she agreed. "You follow me."

She turned and went into the house. Karen followed her through the cool hall into a large empty room with huge glass doors that opened onto a sunken garden. They stood there together, looking out. Karen felt her heart stop.

In the centre of the lawn was a little girl. She was black-haired, with very pale skin and thin features, and she might have been any age between six and ten. Her body was twisted out of its natural shape by a hump which raised one shoulder above the other, and threw her slightly forward. Her legs were too thin to bear any weight. She was sitting on the ground, but as Karen watched, a nurse, who never moved far away, leaned down, assisted her to her feet and supported her into a nearby wheelchair. The movement gave Karen a better look at the girl's face. It was a plain face, childish in shape, but already old with a lifetime of suffering. Then she smiled, and Karen drew in her breath at the fleeting but unmistakeable likeness to her father. The eyes were his, too, dark and lustrous, giving the little girl a touch of beauty.

This was Alicia.

Chapter Eleven

"She is ten years old," said Franca. "No one expected her to live so long, but my Rik, he fight like a tiger for his child. He tell the doctors, 'You keep her alive, or else.' "

She broke off to concentrate on pouring the tea. They were sitting upstairs in the room that was Franca's whenever she stayed overnight in the villa. It had a pair of large French windows which opened onto a balcony overlooking the sunken garden. The two women sat just inside the room, where the breezes of early evening could reach them.

Karen sipped her tea, hardly aware of what she was doing. Fifteen minutes had passed since her discovery, yet even now she was stunned. Somewhere, too deep within her to be easily reached, was a feeling that would eventually be joy. But it was too soon for joy. Her mind whirled with confusion. And tangled with the heart-soaring knowledge that Riccardo did not have a mistress was the realisation that he had not trusted her enough to tell her about his daughter.

"All this time," she murmured, "he told me nothing."

Franca's shrewd old eyes were puzzled. "You never ask him if he have children? Not even when you marry?"

"I thought I knew. Somebody once told me that he had no children."

"Who say that?" Franca demanded suspiciously.

"A friend of mine in England, a journalist."

"Pah!" Franca snorted her contempt. "An Englishman? You think he know? I tell you there is no journalist in the world knows about Alicia. Rik make sure of that. You think he want strangers knowing what he don't tell his own wife?"

"But I didn't just take David's word," said Karen. "Riccardo said the same thing."

"He deny Alicia? I don't believe it," said Franca flatly. "You misunderstood."

"Wait. He said, 'If I do not remarry soon, I shall die childless.' "

Franca nodded sadly. "Always he has known that in the end he will lose Alicia. She will live one more year, perhaps two, not more. But he cling on to her desperately, day by day. He have so few people he can love, who love him—he can't bear to lose her."

"Did he love his wife?" said Karen.

"*Si.* Always. To the end. Even when she was not there anymore. . . ."

"Not there? You mean she left him?"

"Her body did not leave him. But inside she go far away—where he can't reach her."

"You say he loved her," Karen persisted. "But was that why he married her? Didn't she bring him a great dowry?"

Franca choked slightly in her tea. "Where you get these stupid ideas?" she demanded. "Lucia had nothing. Not one lire. Her father was a poor man. He had a small firm. My Alfonso hired him to do some work for the company. Rik went to check the work out and he met Lucia. He was twenty-three. He have girls before, plenty, too many. But Lucia is different. He must marry her."

"My Alfonso get mad. He want Rik to make a great match, big dowry, like you said. Rik win. He say 'I must marry her, and that's it. If you don't like it—you throw me out. I go.' Alfonso give in. He got to. So they get married, and Rik buy this place for Lucia, so he can keep her apart from the family."

"Were they unkind to her?"

Franca made a vague gesture. "They accept her—at last. What use to argue when the wedding has taken place? And Alfonso, he get fond of her. No, it's Rik—he want her to himself. He's possessive. If he love you, you got to belong to him, body and soul. And Lucia is like that. Her day start when he come home. And he—" Franca seemed to search for words. "—if you could see him then, how lonely—always work and trying to please his father. Then, Lucia is like a sun coming out for him. She live only for him, and she want to give him fine, strong sons. Instead . . . " Franca sighed.

"What is wrong with Alicia?"

"Much. She was born this way. Also something wrong with her heart. Up here—" Franca tapped her forehead "—she's normal. Very bright little girl. But the rest of her is as you have seen."

"But aren't there operations that help such children?"

"Not for her. Her heart can't stand it. So she gets worse and worse until—"

"Poor Riccardo. So that's what he meant about dying childless. But did they have no more children?"

"No more. After her daughter is born Lucia become strange—a darkness on her mind. The doctor says is normal, many new mothers like that. It will pass. But it does not pass. She brood about Alicia. She feel that she has failed her husband."

"Did Riccardo feel she had failed him?"

"Never," said Franca emphatically. "He just love her. He says when she is better there will be more children, many sons. And so she starts to get well. Rik love her so much, it is like he is driving the darkness from her mind."

She sighed again, heavily. "I think she would have got well in the end if, if nothing had happened."

Karen drew a sharp breath. It was as though several half-understood hints had come together in her mind.

"This thing that happened," she said quietly, "was it anything to do with Gigi?"

Franca nodded. "Best you know everything," she said. "One night Riccardo take Lucia down to the villa, to have dinner with his parents. Gigi is also to be there, but he does not come. He is only eighteen, but already he is running wild. Alfonso does not esteem him as he does Riccardo, and for this Gigi is jealous, like a child. He is pleased at Riccardo's marriage because it make Alfonso angry. And, God forgive him, I think he is pleased that the baby is not right.

"At the end of the evening Gigi arrives home. He is very drunk—otherwise he would never do what he do. This is what I tell myself, for otherwise there could be no forgiveness for him.

"Alfonso began to shout at Gigi, that he was a disgrace to the family. Why could he not be a credit, like his brother? He should not have said that. Gigi began to scream back, terrible things—about Lucia. He had been asking about her family, and he found out that this had happened before. Lucia didn't know. She thought her child's sickness was an act of God. Now she discover that the taint is in her blood, and this is why she give Riccardo a sick child.

"Gigi yelled, 'Do not hold Riccardo up to me as an example. It was he who defied you, and look at the result. Now our family has a woman who gives birth to—' "

Franca stopped, for she could no longer speak through her tears. Karen was unable to move. She was too horrified by what she was hearing. She wanted to beg Franca to be silent, because she could not endure any more. But she must hear to the end if she was to understand her husband.

"Riccardo knocked his brother down before he could say more," said Franca at last. "But it was too late. I see Lucia's face as she learn that the flaw was in herself, and I knew in that moment that she would never be well again.

"After that the darkness came down once more on her mind. She believed that she was cursed, that she could never give Riccardo a normal child. This is not true. I know that a mother can have a baby like this, and then many other healthy babies. I told her this many times. But by then she was living in another world, and she heard nothing I said."

"Was it true what Gigi said about the family?"

"*Si.* There had been others born this way before. It is a thing that runs in families. But not every child is this way. There had been many normal births in Lucia's family, and the last damaged child had been born twenty years back. That is why she knew nothing.

"She was a lovely creature, frail and sweet. And she loved Riccardo with all her heart. But she had no strength of her own, only what she drew from him. He tried to reach her with his love, but in the end she had to face her despair alone, and she could not do that. Every day she retreated from him a little further. He saw it happen. He grew frantic, trying to draw her back, but nothing was any use. Eventually I think she barely recognised him."

Tears were pouring unchecked down Franca's face. "They had so little time to be happy together, just eighteen months before Alicia was born. They were all the world to each other. I saw him filled with joy for the first time in his life. He would hurry home to be with her. When she was carrying the child he would place his hand on her stomach as though he was touching something sacred. I thought my Rik was safe at last. And then it was all taken away from him.

"He has a father's heart. He consoled himself with Alicia. He gave her all the love that his wife no longer knew how to take. She was a bright little thing, and she knew him from the beginning. He was the first she recognised, and she eased his pain a little. It was about then that I began to spend much time up here. He liked me to be here. He knew his family were safe with me.

"Now it has been this way for years. He turned the villa and its grounds into a fortress where no one could come unless he say. He wanted to protect his wife and daughter completely. No one was allowed here except me—none of his family. But they don't try to come. Alfonso meant well, but he was afraid of sick people. He shut Lucia and Alicia out of his mind. In the end I think he almost forget they exist, it was so long since he saw them. This is how Riccardo wish it to be. Giulietta don't come. She was a child. She never really knew Lucia."

"What about the signora?" asked Karen.

"If Riccardo's *mother,"* said Franca, emphasising the word with malicious relish, "had ever insisted on visiting his wife and child, he would have allowed her to do so, but—" her shrug was eloquent "—she did not insist.

"As for Gigi—I think if he had ever tried to come here, Riccardo would have killed him. He has hated him all these years. He hates him still."

And Gigi hates Riccardo in return, Karen thought, because he is conscious of having done him a great wrong.

"For Alicia," Franca was saying, "he will go anywhere, do anything. That time he went to Milan, she have a nightmare. She dream she die and never see him again. So I call him so she can talk to him. But as soon as she have the phone she is pleading 'Papa, come home.' So he leave whatever he is doing and come back here.

"This has been his world, the only love he has known. Yes, love." Franca broke off with a smile. "I know about the other women. They meant nothing. Riccardo is a normal man. He cannot live as a monk. When he knew that Lucia would never be a wife to him again, he made other arrangements for his needs. There were women for one or two nights, and then no more. It did not hurt Lucia.

She knew nothing. She was safe and protected up here, and besides, her mind grew to be so far away from us that I do not think she would have understood if anyone had told her. But no one ever did."

"Then," said Karen timidly, "it wasn't for that reason that she . . . killed herself?"

"Who say she killed herself?" demanded Franca harshly.

"Gigi."

"Gigi!" Franca almost spat. "Lucia wandered away from the house when no one was watching her. I was not here. The grounds are large. It was two days before we found her. She had drowned in the river. These things happen by accident. No one can say it was suicide. She is buried in consecrated ground. But perhaps—" Franca's shoulders sagged as though she were admitting defeat "—perhaps it is true. No one can say for certain that it was not suicide, and this thought has been an agony for Riccardo ever since. It may be that her torment grew too much for her. Who can say what happened in her mind at the end? Most days she sat and stared blankly at the wall. Sometimes she start weeping, then sit and stare again. I have seen Riccardo talk to her gently for hours, hoping for some sign of a response. But at last even his love could not reach her. Who knows where she went then?

"Since her death he is like the land that the storm has blasted. Everything there is cold, bleak and withered. I think sometimes even his heart has withered, except for Alicia. He has learned to be cruel—perhaps you can turn him back on this path?"

"How can I if he does not trust me?"

Franca spoke urgently. "You must teach him to trust you before it is too late. It is you who must open the way to him. You must reach out, and if he turns away, you must reach out again and again. That is a woman's task."

And I will do it, thought Karen, in silent gratitude. Now

that I know there is no rival I have to fear, I can do anything.

She sat back, suddenly infused with hope. Her path lay clear before her now. She would no longer fear to tell Riccardo of her love. And when he believed her, when he knew about their child, he would forgive her for the past and learn to love her.

Suddenly there came a sound that made both women shoot up in their seats. From down below in the sunken garden, the childish voice had risen in a sharp cry of joy.

"*Papa!*"

"Riccardo!" gasped Karen. "I thought he wouldn't be back for days."

She rose and stepped out onto the balcony. What she saw held her frozen and made a lump come to her throat.

Riccardo was there, kneeling beside the crumpled figure in the wheelchair. His arms were round her, and although his face was hidden, something in the angle of his head told Karen everything about his desperate, fearful love for his child. There was a touching helplessness about the big strong body as it cradled the little broken one.

He took Alicia's face in his hands. Karen could see his features slightly now, enough to make out that there was a light in them that she had never seen before. A wealth of love and anguish lay in the tender way he stroked the little girl's hair back from her forehead and kissed the thin, plain face.

Something contracted painfully in Karen's heart. If only he would hold her with those gentle, possessive hands and look on her with eyes softened with love.

He was talking to Alicia now, his face full of life and interest. When she replied he listened with all seriousness. Karen found herself watching the child. Despite her dreadful deformities she was happy, with the total confidence of one who knows herself cherished beyond price. It was easy to see how she came by this feeling. Riccardo was offering his daughter his complete attention, making a gift of himself, trusting, unwary, his defences down as Karen had never thought to see them, as they had never been for her.

She was about to back quietly away when suddenly the little girl pointed upwards to the balcony. Riccardo's eyes followed her hand, and before she could move Karen found herself caught in his shocked gaze. She could only stare back at him, motionless, while his face went as white as death and closed hard against her in the way she dreaded.

She could have wept. Now he would hate her for discovering his secret, and she would have yet another barrier to pull down before she could reach him.

She backed into Franca's room.

"He's seen me. I must go down to him," she said hurriedly.

"Best thing to happen," said Franca. "No more secrets."

Riccardo was waiting for her at the bottom of the steps, and pulled her into a room off the hall which did not look out onto the sunken garden.

"How *dare* you come here," he said, his face white with fury. "What the devil do you think you are doing to come troubling my daughter?"

She wrenched herself free. "I haven't troubled her. She barely saw me for a moment. She doesn't know who I am."

"How did you get in?"

"Franca let me in."

"And I suppose by now you've prised the story of my life out of her, everything you've no business knowing," he said bitterly. "I should have realised that nothing was safe from your vicious interference."

The injustice of this made her cry out. "I don't want to interfere. But you're my husband. Why should you keep secrets from me?"

"Why should I not? Have you shown that you are to be trusted?"

"You could trust me . . . if only you would," she said forlornly.

He gave a harsh laugh. "And this is how you prove that I can trust you, is it? How did you find this place?"

"I was looking for my passport. I wanted it back. And I came across an envelope—"

"You need say no more," he interrupted her in disgust. "You broke into my desk. A pretty action from a wife."

"Well, it's your own fault," she cried, stung. "Why should I act like a wife when you don't treat me like one?"

"We are wasting time in an exchange of useless reproaches," he said impatiently. "You know very well what is our true situation. I married you because it was necessary to do so. But that is all there is between us."

"But I can't live like that. If we are to spend our lives together I must be more to you than a business convenience. I *must* be. I can't be shut out forever. *I am your wife.*"

He was silent for a moment. The anger seemed to have drained from him, leaving only bleakness behind. When he next spoke there was desolation in his voice.

"There was a time when I believed we would be truly united. In Milan I seemed to have discovered in you—no matter. You were a true woman in my arms, or so I thought. You speak of my shutting you out. When I rose from your bed I felt so close to you that I would have confided the depths of my soul to you. You will say, perhaps, that I should have stayed and ignored that telephone. But for years I have lived with the knowledge that every phone call might contain news about my daughter that I dread to hear. So I cannot ignore a ringing bell as another man could. And I discovered that it was indeed Alicia who needed me.

"When I returned to your room I was going to tell you everything about her, ask for your understanding, even perhaps your love. Who knows? But when I got there—you know what I found, Karen. Of all moments, you picked that one to strike at me, to laugh at me. For this I will never forgive you."

"But I didn't know," she said in despair. "I heard you speak Alicia's name and I thought—"

"I can imagine only too well what you thought," he said harshly. "Though why you should jump to such conclusions—"

"That first night, I heard you talking with your mother . . . about how you wanted me to stay so that you could buy Gigi out. I was angry with you for fooling me. But then you spoke of marrying me, as though I was yours to take for granted. You said you'd have to tell me about Alicia—"

"And you instantly concluded that she was my mistress? Good God! A pretty picture you have of me."

"What else was I to think?" she cried angrily. "You never spoke of having a daughter as any other man would have done. You've shrouded Alicia in secrecy. You've done all you can to convince the world that she doesn't exist. And then you blame me for being taken in. I heard you speak of 'dying childless.' I'm not a mind reader. I think I made a natural mistake.

"I'm sorry for the way I hurt you, Riccardo, truly sorry. But I honestly believe you brought most of it on yourself. You had no right to speak of me as you did to your mother that night, and no right to marry me without telling me you had a child. When you kept quiet at our wedding, of course, I thought she was another woman."

He was looking at her curiously. "And yet you married me," he said in a hard, cold voice. "Hating me, believing me to be deceiving you, you yet married me. Why, Karen? Tell me why. Even before I knew what you have just told me, it was something that puzzled me. Now it becomes totally incomprehensible. Was it the subtlety and ardour of my wooing?"

"*Stop it!*" she screamed, unable to endure another moment of his jeering tones. She pressed her hands over her ears and turned away, but he seized her wrists and yanked her round to face him.

"Tell me what I want to know," he grated. "Tell me before I make you."

Something snapped in her. Hardly knowing what she was doing, she managed to snatch one arm free and lashed out at him. He defended himself and imprisoned her again, shaking her hard.

"*Riccardo!*" Franca's voice screamed from the doorway. "*For God's sake stop it! For the sake of the baby.*"

Karen felt Riccardo's hands stiffen on her shoulders until their clasp was like steel. She looked up into his face and saw violent shock and—did she imagine it?—fear.

He slackened his grip, and she pulled away from him to drop into a chair. She was shaking from head to foot. He stood over her, motionless. It was as though the news had turned him to stone.

"A baby?" he said stupidly.

Franca had come further into the room. Her face was bewildered.

"You knew nothing?" she said to Riccardo.

"I haven't told him, Franca," said Karen in a muffled voice. She could not look up at Riccardo. She feared to meet his eyes.

"We have been married one month," said Riccardo. "How can—?"

"I was carrying the child the day we married," said Karen in a strained voice.

Above her head she heard his sharp intake of breath, and his almost inaudible murmur, "Ah, of course. That is the answer I was seeking."

Then to her amazement he said in a cool, but not unfriendly voice, "What a delightful homecoming. You were saving it to surprise me, weren't you, *cara?*"

Karen saw Franca's face relax into a smile of relief, and

she understood. Riccardo would never hurt the old woman. What he had to say to Karen would be said when they were alone.

"We cannot remain," Riccardo was saying. "I came by only to assure myself that my daughter was well. Also to let you know the news. We found Gigi and Maria in Venice. There was no time to let anyone know. It happened only this morning, and we hastened at once to the airport to depart before the air traffic controllers' strike. Maria has returned home with her father. Gigi has gone to the villa to see our mother. I left as soon as I could." His voice was dry. "I have no taste for the kind of tearful scenes that will now take place for the next few days. I have done my duty in this matter, and now I wish to see it all at an end."

"But for Maria it cannot be ended," said Franca anxiously. "Will her father permit them to marry?"

"He still says not, but—" Riccardo's shrug dismissed the matter. He put his arms round Franca and hugged her. *"Grazie, madre mia,"* he said in a low, moved voice. "Always when I return I thank you, and always I have cause to. Alicia has never looked so well. I will say good-bye to her now, then take Karen home. Tomorrow I shall return and stay longer."

They moved off to the door together. When Franca had gone through, Riccardo turned and looked at Karen.

"Do not attempt to follow me," he said. "I do not wish to see you near my daughter."

A blow across the face would have hurt her less. After waiting a moment to control herself Karen went outside to wait for Riccardo. When she saw him coming she got into her car.

"So this was yours," he said. "I wondered when I did not recognise it."

Franca came down the steps and leaned in at Karen's window to give her a smacking kiss.

"Everything all right now." She beamed.

"Yes, Franca," said Karen with an effort. "Everything will be all right now."

Riccardo reached the apartment five minutes after her.

"What do you have to say to me?" he asked quietly.

"Only that I've been waiting for the right moment to tell you. It never seemed to come."

"I wonder how much longer you would have waited if Franca hadn't forced your hand. Another month? Two? Long enough to persuade me that the child was mine?"

Her eyes opened wide with horror. "Of course it's yours. Riccardo, please, don't say things like that. You can't believe them. It was that night in Milan—"

"Was it? Or was it one of the many happy hours you have spent in the company of Enrico Perioni? Hours I might never have known about but for the chance of Vito's watchfulness?"

"How dare you!"

"Be silent. I have had a most graphic and detailed description of the charming scene that you and Enrico enacted together that night. He was in your arms—"

"I was trying to comfort him—"

"For what?"

"I . . . don't see what that has to do with it," she said desperately.

"I am not a fool, Karen, although you seem to believe that you can treat me as one. That month you disappeared, where did you go? Who were you with? Only Gigi knew. Only Gigi was in your confidence. When you came back from Milan and laughed with him about how you had treated me, did he not introduce you then to his little gigolo friend? Company for your journey, and an extra humiliation for me, since the woman who could go from my bed to that of Enrico Perioni has indeed offered me an insult beyond forgiveness. How you must have laughed, you and Gigi."

"Stop it!" she screamed. *"It isn't true. You don't know what you're saying."*

"And when the little holiday was over," he continued as though he hadn't heard her, "you ditched your boyfriend because you had no further use for him. What Vito interrupted was a little farewell scene, wasn't it Karen? After all, you knew I planned to marry you. You had heard me say so to my mother. And better me than that little parasite.

"And then I played right into your hands. Within three days I arranged our elopement and gave you the chance you needed to pass his child off as mine. You'd have managed it too, but for Franca. No wonder you insisted on changing the marriage settlement to cover a divorce. No wonder you married me without asking me about Alicia. It didn't matter. Marry me for long enough to make his bastard my heir, then leave me, and what? Go back to him? No, I don't think so. You've found out about him now, haven't you Karen? How awkward it must have been for you when he came round again, asking for money."

"Gigi owed him that money."

"Luckily for you, he did. Otherwise you'd have had to find some other story. As it was, I even paid him for you." He broke off and swore violently. "The thought of how you made a fool of me is enough to make me want to kill you."

"Then why don't you?" she said in a hard voice. "It couldn't be worse than what you're doing to me now."

She felt as though her heart had turned to stone. Whatever happened in the future there could be no going back from this moment. She stood quite still, waiting for Riccardo's rage to wear itself out. She would no longer plead for his belief or understanding. That moment was long past.

"Just answer one question, Karen. You never meant to stay married to me, did you?"

After a long moment she looked him in the eyes and said, "No, I didn't."

He turned away as though the last word had been said.

"Wait," she called after him. "You've said what you wanted to. You've abused and insulted me. Now I have something to say about you, and when I've said it I'm leaving you. Because we've come to the end, Riccardo. But before I go, you're going to learn the truth."

She could sense that her cool determination had taken him by surprise, but that didn't matter now.

"The child I'm carrying is yours, Riccardo. You can believe that or not, as you like, but I think you do. I don't think you believe a word of what you've just said. You're clutching at straws because you're angry with me, and you want to put me in the wrong, because you can't face a woman as an equal. You can't ask for her help as one human being to another. You can't admit that you might need her. And that's not a strength, Riccardo, it's a weakness."

She saw him flinch, but she hurried on. If she didn't say it now, she never would.

"I met Enrico Perioni for the first time the night Vito saw us. I'm not going to tell you why I met him because it couldn't make any difference now. But it wasn't through Gigi. Gigi doesn't even know I know him.

"I don't pretend that I haven't been to blame. I made a stupid mistake when I listened to Gigi. But nothing I've done has been through malice. And you haven't behaved too well to me. From the moment I arrived you've tried to manipulate me as though I were a pawn on your chess-board. You even got your mother to invite me here so that you could make me do what you wanted. After I found that out I was bound to fight back. If I did so clumsily, then part of the blame is yours.

"The month I was away Gigi didn't know where I was, and I was alone. I ran away from you in Milan because I thought you were treating me like a—a casual woman. And I couldn't bear it. I loved you, Riccardo, and I still do. I probably always will. But I'll never live with you again because you don't know how to take love.

"I came back to Rome because I began to suspect that I might be pregnant. It was too soon to be more than a suspicion. I didn't have any idea what I was going to do, or how I was going to tell you. When you insisted on our marriage in that way—I couldn't tell you. You were so hostile to me, there's no way I could have said it then. Everything had been wrong between us. I wanted that one thing to be right. But you went on fighting me so hard that the right time never came. If you'd just given me one opening—but you never did."

Karen's voice had become very quiet. She felt as though she was signing her own death warrant.

"It doesn't seem to have struck you, by the way, that Franca has faith in me," she said.

"There are a great many things that Franca doesn't know."

"That's true. But there are also things that she knows by instinct better than either of us. She knows about love, and she knows I've always loved you, and that's why she trusts me. She knew I was pregnant that night at Vito's, and she immediately took it for granted that the child was yours. Because she *knows* I wouldn't deceive you, ever."

Then he did the thing that killed her. Slowly he lifted his head and gave her a long, steady look. And the words he repeated to her were her own.

" 'I could deceive you right under your nose again and again, and you wouldn't see a thing.' Do you expect me to forget that you said that to me, Karen?"

She knew then that it was really over. She said, "Good-bye, Riccardo. I never want to see you again." And left him.

The following evening Karen was still at Leonardo da Vinci Airport. She had arrived the night before to find the controllers' strike just starting. A few planes were getting away, but she couldn't secure a seat on any of them. She stayed the night at the airport hotel.

The following day she considered trying to leave Rome by train, but the air was thick with rumour that the strike would collapse at any moment. So she stayed, and by evening the planes were beginning to fly normally again. If her luck held, hers would depart in about an hour.

She sat alone at a small table in the restaurant, wishing she could stop shaking. The last twenty-four hours had been bad. When you had made a decision that was going to rend you apart and devastate your life you needed to put it into operation quickly, before you had time to brood. The enforced wait, with nothing to do but doubt her own wisdom, had left her drained and exhausted.

But, she reminded herself, she had only the illusion of choice. She had told Riccardo that she was leaving him, but he would certainly have thrown her out anyway. The fact that she had been allowed to get away unhindered was proof that he didn't want her.

For the thousandth time her mind ran through the terrible hour that had followed their last words. She had gone into her room to pack. He did not follow her, and after a few minutes she had heard the front door close. She had left a silent, empty flat. It had been Riccardo's way of saying that she no longer existed for him.

She looked down at the sealed envelope that she held in her lap. Before leaving she would post it. She wondered what Riccardo would make of its contents. They would certainly surprise him.

What was he doing this minute? Was he with Alicia? Probably. He had said that he would return to the villa today to avoid all the tedious family scenes.

"May I sit down?"

At first she thought she must have imagined his voice, but when she looked up Riccardo was really standing there. He looked haggard and ill, and also—unbelievably—unsure of himself.

She moved to make room for him, and for a few moments they sat in silence. He did not look at her.

"I was afraid I might have missed you," he said at last.

"My plane leaves very soon. I expect it to be called at any moment."

"Have you checked in? Is your luggage gone?"

"Yes."

"Will you tell them, please, that you are not travelling and wish your luggage returned to you?"

The words were almost the same ones he might have used at any time in the past, but something told Karen that he was speaking very carefully. She answered with equal care.

"No. I don't see any reason to do that. I told you why I was leaving you. Nothing has changed."

He looked at his hands. "For you, perhaps, nothing has changed. But for me . . ." He stopped a passing waiter and ordered himself a brandy. He was silent until it came. Then he said, "I have been with Giulietta and Pietro today."

"I thought you were going to keep out of the family scenes."

"This one I could not avoid. Pietro called me and demanded your presence."

"*My* presence?"

"Yes. He has complaints against you. When I told him you were not there he made them to me. He says that you assisted his wife in a clandestine relationship."

If Riccardo knew this much, then surely he must know the whole truth about Enrico. Karen waited for the weight to lift from her heart and gladness to take its place. But nothing happened.

"I only helped her to end it," she said at last. "Giulietta didn't want to see him again, so—"

"Yes. Giulietta has told me this herself. It appears that Maria spent most of yesterday evening pouring out her spite against my sister. In the end Giulietta was no longer able to deny the accusations, and the story came out. That is how I come to know the truth about your meetings with Enrico."

He took another sip of brandy, and said in an almost inaudible voice, "Why did you not tell me yourself? I can understand your loyalty to my sister, but surely the saving of our marriage comes first?"

"I don't think it had anything to do with Giulietta," said Karen honestly. "It was more that I realised that we had no marriage to save. You were so anxious to think the worst of me, so determined not to give me the benefit of the doubt. You always have been, and I can't face any more of it."

"You plan to take my child away from me? Perhaps my son?" He spoke without looking at her.

"*Your* child? Yesterday nothing would induce you to believe that it was yours."

"There is something more. The month you were away, Giulietta was constantly in Enrico's company. Maria has said so, and Giulietta has admitted it."

"Which means he wasn't with me."

"Please, Karen, let me finish. This is hard enough. You have all the advantages over me. Franca has also said that she saw you on the night of your return, and that you told her then that you might be carrying my child."

"So I'm cleared," she said bitterly. "You believe me because Franca says I'm telling the truth, and because Giulietta says I am. But you don't believe me when *I* say I am. My word alone isn't good enough for you, Riccardo. Well, that's not good enough for *me*. I can't spend my life with a man who won't trust me unless I can produce witnesses for the defence."

Before he could speak there was an announcement over the loudspeaker. It was the first call for her flight. Riccardo laid a hand on her arm.

"Karen, wait, please. Let me finish what I have to say. I have come here to ask you not to give up so easily.

Perhaps there can never be peace between us, but we are to have a child. For the sake of that child I am asking you to set aside our differences."

It was as if a knife had turned inside her. He wanted her, but only for the sake of the baby. As if to reinforce that impression he added, "I do not wish my son to be born in a foreign land."

She looked down at his hand, which was still on her arm.

"Are you going to try to stop me by force?" she asked.

He removed his hand as though she had burned him.

"There is no question of force. I am offering you a bargain. I will not attempt to command you, Karen. I have been too greatly humbled for that. I will only say that if you will remain with me, you can do so on your own terms."

He was humbled. He had said it. She had dreamed of this since that first night in Vito's when his subtlety and arrogance had got the better of her. And now the moment had come when she had least expected it. The battle was over, and she had won. Victory was ashes in her mouth.

"It's no use," she said at last. "There are no terms you could offer me that would make our marriage endurable. It's too late for that."

"Do not make me plead with you, Karen."

She looked at him squarely. "No, that would be beneath you, wouldn't it? You prefer making a bargain about 'terms.' Don't worry. I don't want you to plead with me. I've made my decision. I love you, Riccardo. You could have had me back without any terms if you'd really wanted me, if you'd had any *need* of me in your heart. But you've always tried to make it clear that you haven't. You've shut me away from the centre of your life and kept me on the outside. But I can't live there.

"You don't want me. Not really. What you want is the firm, and your son—if there is one. Well, I shan't try to take either of them away from you. You can see your baby whenever you're in London, and if it's a boy I'll send him to you later, and you can teach him as Alfonso taught you.

"As for the firm—here." She thrust the envelope into his hand. "It's a letter to the lawyer. I've told him that despite our separation I want you to keep control. I don't know if I've worded it in the right way, but if I haven't, tell him to send me the necessary documents, and I'll sign them."

She waited for him to say something, but he only sat staring blankly at the envelope in his hand.

"So it's over, isn't it?" she said. "We've fought each other to a standstill, and you've got what you wanted all the time."

She rose and gathered her things together. He got to his feet and left the restaurant with her. He was walking like a man in a dream, and she wondered if he'd really heard anything she said. She stopped in front of him.

"Don't come any further with me," she said.

"Karen—"

"Good-bye, Riccardo. God bless you."

She touched his cheek with a gentle hand, then, moved by a sudden impulse, leaned forward and kissed him. She hurried away quickly and then looked back at the door to the departure lounge. He was still standing where she had left him, his expression that of a man who has received a stunning, unexpected blow. Then she turned away and bumped into someone because she could no longer see clearly.

Chapter Twelve

It was midnight when she landed at Heathrow to find the weather cold and wet. Italy seemed a million light years away.

She took a taxi to her London house. The lights were on as she entered, telling her that Jane, her assistant, was still there, working. When enthusiastic greetings had been exchanged, Jane made her stretch out on the sofa while she made some tea and sandwiches. Looking round her, Karen wondered if she had ever been away.

"What are you doing working here at this hour?" she asked when she had drunk her tea and felt better.

"Oh, things have piled up on me rather," said Jane vaguely.

"What about that girl we hired just before I went? Doesn't she ease the burden?"

"She turned out to be lazy and stupid, so I fired her," said Jane, chuckling. "I'd get messages three weeks late, that kind of thing. I put up with it until two days ago, when your picture appeared in some magazine. . . . Here." Jane reached over and rummaged in a pile to bring out a continental news magazine.

Karen studied the picture, which showed her and Riccardo together for the opening of the Rome Opera. It had been taken just as they entered the foyer. Her heart stopped as she saw Riccardo's face, handsome and smiling. He was looking down at her with an expression of pride that she did not remember noticing at the time. She realised afresh the finality of the step she had taken, and her throat constricted. And yet she knew she had done the right thing. Riccardo had come to her too late, and saying the wrong things. There was no hope for them.

"You fired her because of this?" she said. "I don't understand."

"She looked at it and said, 'Oh, he found her then?' I said what did she mean, and she said, 'That's the bloke that came here looking for her that time you were away.' "

"What?" Karen was thunderstruck.

"That's what I said. Apparently he was here six weeks ago. I was away for a few days doing a location job, and she was taking messages. He came knocking at this door, asking for you."

Karen sat back, feeling her heart beating painfully. Six weeks ago. That was when she had been driving around Italy. So that was why Riccardo was missing from Rome. He had come to England, looking for her.

"I'd always told her," Jane went on in a cross voice, "that if anyone wanted you she was to take their name and number and I'd call them back. She said it wasn't her fault because he wouldn't give a name, or anywhere he could be contacted. But even so, she should have told me, not just forgotten all about it. Anyway, it wasn't just that. She was lazy and stupid, and always late. So I fired her."

"Did you give her time to tell you anything about what she said to him before you threw her out?" said Karen.

"She suggested he try David Brightwell, but that was all she could think of. I've been trying to call you these last couple of days, but I could never find you in. Anyway, it doesn't seem to matter much, since you evidently found each other in the end."

Found each other. Karen pondered the phrase. That was exactly what she and Riccardo had failed to do, and in the end they had lost each other forever.

She wondered what he had thought about being referred to David Brightwell. The next day she called David, but was informed by his answering machine that he was in Scotland on holiday. She left a message for him to call her when he returned, and two days later he rang. They had dinner together.

"You look older," he said at once. "Not just two months, more like a hundred years."

"Thank you." She laughed at his matter-of-fact tone.

"No, I don't mean that you're not just as lovely, in fact you're more so. But your face is thinner, and it looks as if it's been lived in."

"Well, you did warn me, didn't you?" she said lightly.

"I tried to. But since you married him, I assumed all my warnings had been in vain."

"David—"

"It's all right," he said hurriedly. "You explained everything in your letter. In fact, you gave away a lot more than I think you realise. When a woman's that crazy about a man. . . ."

"I don't think I said anything about being crazy about him," she said frostily.

"No, you were very businesslike. Quite unlike you. But it was there between every line. It was the same with him. He was in a great rage, apparently because the firm was going through a crisis—something to do with a stretch of land—and your disappearing act was making life more difficult. But that wasn't his only reason for looking for you, whatever he might have wanted me to believe."

"You saw him then? I wondered. . . ."

"He turned up one evening, barged into my flat and practically accused me of hiding you in the bedroom. I was packing to go to Scotland, and I had a job convincing him my trip wasn't our honeymoon. I think he was on the point of murdering me."

"Probably," said Karen in a bleak voice. "If I'd married you, my share of the firm would have fallen even further outside his control. He'd cheerfully have killed you before allowing that."

David gaped at her. "Are you seriously asking me to believe that he married you for your money?" he demanded.

"You could put it that way, although he left me in no doubt that I could keep as much of my own money as I wanted. It was the power he was interested in."

"He told you that?"

"Yes."

"And you believed him?"

"Why shouldn't I?"

"You're a fool, Karen," he said bluntly. "The biggest fool in creation. A man doesn't get into that kind of state over a few shares."

"You don't know this man."

"I know jealousy when I see it. Tornese was in a black hell of jealousy. He didn't just want to know about our relationship now. He wanted to know about the past. I was really put through the third degree. I did finally manage to persuade him that we'd never been lovers, but it was far from easy. And why should he care, if all he was bothered about was his firm?"

Karen was silent, her mind in turmoil.

"Why didn't you contact me and let me know about this?" she said at last.

"I tried to. The minute he'd gone I put through a call to his mother's home, where you were supposed to be staying. But you'd left and no one knew where you were. I rang back several times, but it was always the same. Then the last time I called I found myself speaking to this woman who said you'd gone to Arella to marry her son,

Riccardo. After that it didn't seem so important to tell you, since events had plainly overtaken us. Then I got your letter, forwarded on from my flat, saying you'd married him, and besides, I had something on my own mind by that time." He gave her a self-conscious grin.

"What's she like?" said Karen, pleased for him.

"Scottish. We met mountain-climbing. She fell off this rock straight into my arms."

For the rest of the meal she encouraged him to talk about his lady love, glad to have a clear conscience where David was concerned.

She lay awake for a long time that night, mulling over what she had heard, wondering if it would have made any difference if she'd known earlier. She decided that it wouldn't. David was convinced that Riccardo loved her, but there wasn't a single thing in her husband's behaviour that couldn't be explained some other way. Even his insistence on knowing about her past life was simply the sexual jealousy of a man who has possessed a woman and wants exclusive ownership.

Again and again she ran through her mind their last moments together in the airport. Riccardo knew that she loved him. She had told him so. But he had been unable to force any words of love past his lips, even to keep her. When she had given him the power he wanted and promised him access to their child, he had let her go.

She tortured herself by imagining their life together if she had returned to him. 'You can make your own terms' he had said. Wouldn't she have been more sensible to make those terms? She knew now that he had no mistress. He was ashamed of his behaviour towards her, and she had him at a disadvantage. A clever woman should have been able to make use of that.

But she was too much in love with Riccardo to be clever where he was concerned. It was easy to lie there and make calculations in her head, but she would never have been able to put them into practise. One look at him and her heart would turn over; his lightest touch could make her bones melt. And she would have given herself back to a man who neither loved nor wanted her, and who had shown as much with devastating thoroughness.

As their separation lengthened her need of him tormented her. She would wake, aching, reaching out to find him, only to discover a cold empty space in the bed. Then she would bury her face in her pillow and sob violently until she slept.

Weeks passed without any word from him. From the lawyer there came no acknowledgement of her letter.

Giulietta wrote to say that she was still living under her husband's roof, but nervous of what every day might bring. The strangest thing of all, she said, was that she owed it to Riccardo that she had not been thrown out. It was Riccardo who had told Pietro to consider that he might himself have been at fault. Giulietta was fearful of what would happen in a month's time, when Riccardo had to leave Rome for a conference in Brussels that would last for two weeks. She feared that, without her brother's influence, Pietro's anger would rise again.

Pietro had still not consented to Maria's marriage to Gigi, but Giulietta suspected that soon it would become inevitable. Any day now the girl's condition would be confirmed. Maria certainly thought so. She went around looking cheerful. . . .

Karen threw the letter down, pitying Maria with all her heart. She had had time recently to go back over what she knew of Gigi, and to see what a large part he had played in her misfortune. There was the conversation they had had in her apartment that first day, when she had spoken Alicia's name, and he had answered her questions so cunningly. On the whole he had confined himself to the facts, and yet . . .

He knew what I was thinking, she told herself bitterly. I made it only too obvious. He could have told me the truth at any time, and he carefully avoided it.

It had been in Gigi's interests to keep her and Riccardo as far apart as possible, and his methods had been completely unscrupulous. Not that she knew the basis of his hatred for his brother, with its roots in jealousy and shame, she could see more clearly the tentacles of his spite spreading over Riccardo's life. She understood Riccardo's savage reaction when he thought she was teaming up with his brother. She could see the filial love with which, for his mother's sake, he had tried to smother his dislike of Gigi, and his pain when his mother repaid his efforts by her shortsighted championing of her wastrel younger son.

If only I had known, she whispered to herself. I could have helped him; I might even have taught him to love me. But now it is too late.

Her pregnancy was showing very little, but every day she grew more aware of the child—Riccardo's child, a never-ending reminder of what she had had and lost.

About a month after her return she had dinner with David Brightwell and Sheila, his Scottish girl friend. She found her to be a pleasant, unsophisticated girl, overwhelmed at the prospect of the foreign trip she was about to take with David.

"I keep telling her not to expect too much," said David when they were alone for a moment. "It's a working trip, not a holiday. Anything more boring than a conference in Brussels I can't imagine, but—"

"David, did you say Brussels?"

"Yes. There's a big Common Market conference next week. All the heads of the major European industries will be there. Why? Do you think—?"

He stopped. Karen had never told him the full story of her return, but it was obvious to him that something had gone badly wrong with her marriage.

"Yes, I believe my husband intends to be there," said Karen.

Luckily, at that moment Sheila returned and the subject

was dropped. Karen saw neither of them again before they departed for Brussels. She began to read all the papers, and her heart skipped a beat when she read that television cameras would be at Brussels. She promised herself that she would be strong-willed, but on the day the conference opened she sat glued to the set. She had to wait until evening before she saw him, and then it was only for a brief moment as he was entering a huge, anonymous building. Then he was gone, and she was left aching with misery.

After that she watched every news bulletin, waiting for the fleeting seconds when he appeared. She searched for some sign that he was suffering as she was, but there was no change in him. His face was thin, but then it always had been. And the air of tension he emanated was also familiar to her, and probably connected with his work.

David rang once to say that he had seen Riccardo. They were staying in the same hotel.

"Not that we spoke. But he recognised me, because he gave me a long, hard look that made me very glad I had Sheila with me," he said, chuckling. "I put my arm round her just to make my point clear. He's one man I don't want to have a punch-up with."

"You wouldn't," said Karen. "He's Italian. He believes in poison, the subtle weapon that kills from within."

"I beg your pardon?" he said, bewildered.

"Never mind. I was quoting someone."

"You mean I should be careful if he offers me something to drink?"

"Be especially careful if he offers you a choice of eating or drinking," she said with wry humour.

"Karen, what on earth are you burbling about?"

"Nothing. I'm just getting lightheaded. 'Bye David."

The conference split into groups, one for each major industry. The electronics firms attracted most attention, as theirs was the industry moving ahead the fastest. Disputes developed and attracted a lot of news coverage. Karen heard Riccardo's name spoken so often that she became almost inured to the little stab of pain it gave her.

On the Monday of the second week of the conference she settled down to watch a lengthy news programme which was to devote itself entirely to the events in Brussels. She listened impatiently to the opening preamble by the newsman, outlining the way the conference had gone so far and discussing the acrimonious debates that were taking place in the electronics section.

"But only half an hour ago," said the reporter, "the conference was rocked by the sudden departure of Signor Riccardo Tornese. There had been nothing in his previous behaviour to indicate that he might leave. He had appeared to be persuading the other delegates to his point of view, and although it was known . . ."

Karen's heart was in her mouth. She began flicking feverishly through radio channels to see if she could learn more. But there was only the endless repetition of the statement that Riccardo had walked out and refused to speak to anyone. At the end of an hour she returned to the television programme, which was just winding up.

"There is still no news about Signor Tornese's abrupt departure, which has shaken this assembly to its roots. No reasons have been given, and reporters have been warned against approaching him. What we have here now is a shambles with no one knowing . . ."

She switched off the set and sat there, shaking. With all her heart she longed to pick up the phone and call Riccardo. Perhaps she alone could guess why he had gone. He had been called home by some crisis concerning Alicia, the one person in all the world who had the power to move him. Now, if ever, she should be with her husband.

But she stopped her hand on its way to the phone. Into her mind, unbidden, came the memory of Riccardo, turning to her in the doorway that day she had gone to see

Alicia and saying, "Do not attempt to follow me. I do not wish to see you near my daughter."

Her hand fell. There was no way she could go to him after that prohibition. Not unless he invited her. And he would never do that.

The abrupt ringing of the phone shattered her. She snatched it up with a jerky movement, her heart filled with a frantic prayer. But the caller was David.

"Have you heard the news?" he said faintly.

"Yes. I've just switched off. Do you know anything, David?"

"I think I'm about the only person who does. The oddest thing has just happened. Ever since Tornese walked out he's been practically surrounded by body-guards to keep journalists away. But about ten minutes ago I got a message saying that I was to go to his hotel room. I found him packed and ready to go. It was clear that he'd only been waiting for me. He said he was going to tell me what he'd told no one else."

"What did he tell you?" Karen's hand was clutching the receiver so hard that her knuckles were white.

"He said he wasn't leaving because of anything to do with the conference, but because his daughter was dying. I never knew he had a daughter. . . ."

"Yes, yes. Go on."

"That's it. He said she'd been sick for years, and now she wasn't expected to live the night. Frankly, I was sceptical. How come nobody's heard of this girl? I hinted that I had my doubts, and he looked at me very oddly, and said I could always check the truth of what he'd told me. Karen, do you think he meant me to—"

"Yes!" said Karen, speaking through her tears. "You've done exactly what he meant you to do."

"Well, why couldn't he just call you himself?"

"Because for him that would be impossible. I can't explain now. I have to rush. But David, please—I beg you—don't use this story."

"Not use it? You dare say that to a hardened old reporter like me? It's the best story since—"

"David, if you ever had any affection for me, I implore you, don't crucify him by printing this."

He gave a little sigh. "If it really matters that much—"

"It does, David. It matters more than anything ever has."

"Then I suppose I'll have to do it. Good luck. And be careful flying in your condition."

She gasped. "How did you know?"

"Be off with you, Karen, or you'll miss the next plane to Rome."

It was noon the following day when she landed at Leonardo da Vinci Airport. As soon as she was through customs she jumped into the hired car that was waiting for her and began the drive to Monte d'Este. She was assailed by doubts. Had she read too much into Riccardo's action? Had he really chosen this way of sending her a message? Wouldn't he just have picked up the phone and called?

By the time the villa was in sight she had convinced herself that she was wrong to come. Riccardo did not wish her to be here; he would be angry with her. Fear coiled in her stomach, but she forced herself on.

She saw Riccardo's car standing before the house, and Franca's. The front door was pulled open as she ran up the steps, as though someone had been watching for her. She ran across the hall to where Franca was standing. For a moment the two women looked at each other, then a hoarse voice called from above, *"Franca, is that her? Is she here yet?"*

At once she was flying up the stairs. After the dazzle of the sun she was blinded, so that at first she did not see the gaunt, haggard figure who stepped out of the shadows and loomed over her. She only felt his strong arms go round her in a fierce embrace, felt his face press into the curve of her neck as though he were seeking refuge, and knew that she was where she belonged.

After a very long time he raised his head and looked down at her.

"In my worst nightmares," he said, "you did not come. . . ."

Without another word he took her hand and led her along the corridor to Alicia's room. Karen's eyes opened wide when she saw it. It was a little girl's room, but it was also fitted out with all the latest hospital equipment. A doctor and nurse hovered by the bed, never taking their eyes from the girl who lay slightly on her side, breathing painfully.

He went and resumed his seat near the bed, where he could see the child's face. Karen sat beside him. He did not look at her again, and she might almost have thought he had forgotten her but for the painful pressure on her hand, which he did not release.

Franca came in and whispered that a room was ready and waiting for her. A few minutes later a maid entered with coffee and rolls. Karen managed to eat and drink with only one hand. Not for the world would she have withdrawn her hand from the man who sat beside her, apparently oblivious of her presence, yet desperately depending on her.

After a while she heard a slight change in his breathing and looked up to see that his head had fallen forward onto his chest.

"That is good," said Franca softly. "He make himself stay awake every moment, but now you are here he sleeps. He say to me many times, 'I will sleep when she comes.' I say, 'Suppose she don't come.' He say, 'She will come. I know it.' "

"How bad is the child?" said Karen. "I heard she was dying."

"The doctor says she is calmer. Perhaps she live this

time, but for how long? One day soon she die. My Rik know that. Better now you're here."

Riccardo dozed for an hour and woke with a start. His eyes flashed at once to the bed where the crumpled figure was still fighting for her life. But she was breathing, and the sound was slightly stronger now.

"Her condition has stabilised," said the doctor in a firm voice. "You can do no good by remaining here, signore. You should go and sleep properly. If there is any change I will call you."

"No," said Riccardo at once. "I will remain here. But you—" he looked at Karen "—you have travelled all night."

"I'm staying with you," she said firmly.

He did not reply, but the look in his eyes made her glad of her decision, although her body ached with weariness.

The light in the room was fading. Evening came faster now that it was November. Soon it was almost dark. Still Riccardo sat with Karen's hand in his. She stole a look at him. He was unshaven, and there were black marks under his eyes.

She had often pictured their possible reunion and wondered how it might be. And now here it was, unlike anything she had ever dreamed of. Riccardo was exhausted and too distracted with grief to speak much to her. But he clung to her, and he was hers in a way he had never been before. He had told her, without words, of his need.

At midnight there came a change. The little girl began to stir, as though strength was flowing back into her limbs. The doctor took her pulse and his face lightened perceptibly. Karen became aware of the painful tension in her husband's alert figure.

"I think," said the doctor carefully, "that we have weathered this one. How long the little girl will maintain her improvement is uncertain, but for the moment . . ."

No one was listening to him. Alicia had opened her eyes

and was smiling directly at her father. He knelt beside her bed, stroking her face with gentle fingers, as though he feared to touch her. Franca was weeping noisy tears of joy. Karen looked round and felt a little ache come into her heart at how completely she had been forgotten. She no longer belonged here. She went to the door.

"Will you show me which is my room please?" she said to the maid she found outside.

She found her case unpacked and her things laid out on the bed. After a quick shower she slipped on her night-dress and slid between the sheets, grateful for their cool smoothness. But she had hardly put the light out when the door opened and Riccardo was standing beside the bed.

"Why did you go?" he demanded urgently. "I looked for you and you weren't there." He dropped to one knee beside the bed.

"I wasn't sure you needed me anymore," she said.

"I shall always need you, as long as I have life. Oh, Karen." He buried his face against her. She put her arms fiercely around him, stroking his head with hands that were loving and protective.

"I have needed you all this time," he said. "I have longed for you in the night and awakened cursing myself for letting you go, simply because I could not find the words to say that you were necessary to me. I told myself that you would come back because you would hear my heart calling to you. But I could not force myself to lift the phone and ask you. I believed that it was for you to come to me and ask me to take you back. But you never did.

"When my daughter became ill I yearned for you more than ever, but after what I had said to you—I was afraid that you would not return."

"But you knew that I would," she reminded him. "Franca said so."

"I told Franca I believed it, but in my heart I was never sure. I knew I did not deserve your forgiveness. I should have called you myself, but I could not. I feared to speak to you."

"Why should you fear me?" she said wonderingly.

"Because I have done everything to deserve your hatred. Because I denied my love for you—denied it to you and to myself. There is no greater crime."

"You love me?" she whispered.

"Since the first evening, the first moment I think, when I saw you standing beneath my father's portrait, and I knew why he had sent you to me."

"He?"

"Of course. My father was never wrong about people. Do you think he did not know that we should love each other?"

"But how could he?"

"Because he knew you, and he knew me. He knew what I needed. He said to me once, 'You need a woman who can look you in the eye and tell you to stop your nonsense, not one who will treat everything you say like the word of God. That will only encourage your conceit.' I denied it, but when I met you that first night I knew my father had been right and he had found me that one woman.

"But I foolishly allowed myself to become overconfident. I was very sure of myself at the end of the first evening. I thought it was all going to be easy."

"It might have been if I hadn't overheard you talking to your mother," she said. She related the conversation more fully this time. He groaned.

"What a conceited lout you must have thought me."

"Yes," she said without hesitation. "I was furious with you. That was why I kept quiet about my Italian and joined forces with Gigi."

"Then why did you vote me chairman? You had it in your power to spoil my life, why didn't you use it?"

His arms were wound tightly round her now, and she rested her head against his shoulder as she spoke.

"I don't really know," she said, "except that when it came to the point, I couldn't. I wasn't fooled by Gigi, although I didn't know the worst of him then. All I realized was that he was being spiteful, and I didn't want to be spiteful too. And it meant so much to you. . . ."

"All the more reason, surely, to take it away from me and show me that you were stronger than I was." He was tense as he spoke.

"But that wasn't so important, Riccardo. I fought you only because I had to defend myself. In my heart I only wanted you to love me, as I love you."

His mouth was on hers before she had finished speaking, moving slowly and with infinite tenderness. When she could no longer breathe, he drew back and looked down at her.

"And what do you believe now?" he said.

"I'll believe anything you tell me," she whispered.

"Will you believe that I love you, after the way I have treated you? That I have loved you so much it scared me. I could never endure to be in anyone's power, Karen, and my heart has been in thrall to you from the first moment. It seemed important to prevent you from finding out, although now I cannot remember why. That night in Arella, when you made love to me, I became frightened. You had come so close to discovering my weakness. I had to fight you off before you demolished the fragile defences I had erected against you.

"I should have known then that there is no safety in love. One must be brave, and risk putting his faith in his beloved, and that I was afraid to do."

"But surely you guessed that I loved you?"

"No, you little witch! How could I, when you were always playing me off against my brother? When you came home late that night with Gigi I could have killed you both. If you had truly been in his bed I think I would have done. But when I kissed you I knew that you had not."

"Just the same," she murmured, "it's lucky for me that the waiter called you the next morning and confirmed that we'd been at the gaming club."

"No, I swear it. I would take your word in the face of any evidence. You are not a woman who deceives."

"You said that to me once before, and I was fool enough to tell you—"

He stroked her hair. "You spoke in anger. I should not have thrown those words back at you, but I was filled with rage. You had concealed my child from me, and discovered my most painful secret. And again you had shown me the thing above all things that I did not wish to face—how vulnerable I was to you. I lashed out with any weapon I could."

"I didn't dare tell you about our child. You were so angry with me. But I always wanted to tell you. That's why I came back."

"Where were you all that time?"

"Just driving round Italy, trying to forget you. Not succeeding." She felt his arms tighten convulsively round her. "Gigi didn't know where I was, whatever he may have led you to think. But I was wrong to sign everything over to him. I should have thought what I was doing. Forgive me, Riccardo."

His lips sought hers again. "We each have much to forgive the other," he murmured. "Perhaps you will never forgive *me* for the manner of our marriage, but I was scared. I had to make sure of you. I thought that in Milan—"

She gave a soft, contented chuckle. "You planned what happened in Milan, didn't you?"

"It is true that I took you there with the intention of securing you to myself while there was still time. Instead . . ." He broke off and his arms tightened round her. She could feel the anguish that still shook him at the memory of the blow she had dealt him that night.

"I heard you talking to Alicia," she said hurriedly. "You were going to leave me and go to her, and I thought . . ."

He laid a hand gently over her mouth to silence her. The time had not yet come when they could speak of that night without pain.

"I used any excuse I could find to force you to marry me," he resumed. "I did not know how far your alliance with my brother might have gone. I was even afraid you might marry him to spite me after what happened in Milan. That thought was a nightmare to me."

"Yes, I can imagine. The thought of Gigi getting all that control—"

"Hush," he said, his mouth in her hair. "You know my true meaning. The thought of you as his wife, in his arms, gradually learning your terrible mistake—I would have committed murder to free you."

After a moment's hesitation he said, "You must understand about Alicia. Much of my life must be spent here with her."

"Then let us live here," she begged. "Oh, Riccardo, please don't shut me out again. If you do, I shall know I'm not truly your wife."

"You are my wife," he said softly. "You are the wife of my heart, my soul and my body. There will never be another woman. If you can share this part of my life, then truly you will have joined yourself with me."

"You think she will live this time?"

"I am sure of it. After you left she spoke to me. Her voice was strong. All will be well."

He undressed and slipped into bed with her. He took her into his arms, and they had their true reconciliation, sweet, loving, wordless. Afterwards he slept while she clasped him in her arms, the weight of his head pillowed between her breasts, until peace seemed to descend on her, and she too slept.

It was daylight when she woke, and she was alone. For a

moment she had the old sad feeling that she used to get when she woke by herself in the apartment. She felt oddly nervous about meeting Riccardo again. It was as though the events of the previous night had all been a dream, and she would wake to find him hostile to her, as before.

She rose and went to the window. But before she could open the shutters, the door opened behind her and he came in. He seemed to relax at the sight of her.

"Alicia?" she said, knowing that this would please him.

"She is better still. We have talked, and she is eating something." He came close and stood with his hands on her shoulders, looking her over as if trying to fix her image in his mind. "I was afraid I would come back and find you gone," he said at last. "I've dreamed so often that you came back to me, but then I woke and found myself alone." His grip tightened. "I shall never permit you to leave me again, my darling, not if I have to keep you here with a ball and chain."

She laughed joyfully, for she could see that a night's sleep and the lifting of his cares had restored him to himself. The weary, desperate man who had turned to her the previous night was gone. In his place was the arrogant lover she had always known. And yet something was different. There was a warmth in his eyes that she had never seen there before.

"You're staying here now, do you hear?" he demanded, embracing her fiercely. "I should never have let you walk off at the airport."

"Why did you?" she teased him between kisses.

"I didn't know what to say to you. I offered you any terms you liked, I was so desperate to keep you. No other woman has ever been able to dictate terms to me. But I had to make it a bargain—I couldn't plead with you."

No, he would never do that. He was a proud man. Yet with that subtle indirectness for which Italians were famous, he had contrived to let her know his need of her, and she had responded as he had known she would. So it would always be. He would expect his woman to understand him, but if she failed to do so, he would never beg.

"When you let me go, I thought it was because you didn't really want me," she said.

"I could hardly face you. You'd spoken to me with such contempt the night before, and then, when I knew you were telling me the truth about the child, I saw myself through your eyes, and I didn't like what I saw. When you put the envelope into my hands, I didn't know what to do, or say. I tried to tell myself that it was all I wanted, but when you walked away from me, I knew I'd gained nothing and lost everything." He smiled suddenly. "Here."

He thrust his hand into his dressing-gown pocket and pulled out an envelope that she recognised as the one she had given him.

"So that's why I never heard from the lawyer," she cried. "I always wondered."

"I never gave it to him. And tomorrow we visit him and you resume power over what is your own."

"You mean that?"

"I mean it. In future we face each other in the boardroom as equals."

She looked at him frowning. He read her expression accurately and gave a faint smile. "This is not another trick, *cara*. My word of honour."

"Then why are you doing it?" she asked.

"For many reasons." He paused, then seemed to force himself on with great difficulty. "I once accused you of harming the firm to satisfy your own pride and your desire to revenge yourself on me. But after you had gone I realised that I had done exactly the same thing, at least potentially."

"I don't understand."

"I began to ask myself what would be your position if anything should happen to me, and I was filled with shame at how defenceless I had left you. In the event of my death much power would return to you, but you know nothing of the firm because since our marriage I have excluded you. I should have protected you by teaching you everything I knew. Instead, in my pride and anger, I shut you out. Your ignorance would have made you Gigi's victim again. And the blame for anything that happened then would have been entirely mine."

Tears stung her eyes. Only she knew what such an admission cost him, but he had forced himself to make it because he was generous and honest—and because he trusted her. She flung her arms round his neck.

"Besides," he said as he hugged her, "this is something that has to come. My father recognised that fact before I did. He was always a man of vision."

"And you?"

"Be a little patient with me, *cara*. It is still very strange for me to see a woman in a position of power. I shall teach you—but I shall also learn from you."

"You'll never be able to keep it up," she predicted. "You'll be furious the first time I disagree with you."

"Of a certainty I shall. But I do not recall that you are afraid of my anger."

"We'll fight—"

"All our lives. But always with honour. And after every fight there will come a sweet reconciliation."

His mouth was on hers. The probing of his tongue distracted her so skillfully that she scarcely realised he was pulling down the straps of her nightdress until his lips burned a trail down her neck to her breasts. She clung to him, feeling the thin material fall about her feet.

He drew her down onto the bed, running his hands reverently over her, touching the slight, almost imperceptible swell.

"Mine," he said softly, and took her into his arms. Their kiss was long and deep, and when they drew apart, he said in a voice that was almost inaudible, "Love me, my wife."

Even now it took all her courage to open her arms to

him in invitation, but he came to her easily, only holding back a little so that he could watch her face with brooding eyes as she slipped the dressing gown from him and ran her hands over his naked frame. It was as though she were discovering his body for the first time, the wide shoulders, the long spine, the swell of his flanks, and the powerfully muscled thighs.

He seemed to be holding his breath, trying to read something in her touch, but at last its message of sweet possessiveness reached him. The smile he gave her then made her heart turn over. She began to tremble, but he made love to her as never before. The arms that held her were as gentle as a child's. When the pleasure became frightening she could look into his eyes and see there not only passion, but the security of a love that held her fast.

He took her with tender, loving strength, not demanding, but waiting for her to offer. Once he had rejected her gifts. Now he sought them eagerly, revelling in the riches she showered on him.

"I didn't know," he said at last in a shaken voice. "I never dreamed . . ."

"It's true," she promised him. "It will always be true."

He dozed again with his head on her breast, resting like a man who has come to the end of a long journey. She held him against her as she looked down the long years ahead of them. There would be difficult years sometimes. He was still a proud man, who feared the depths of his own feelings for her. It would be for her to teach him to overcome that fear.

She saw also what she knew he had not yet faced, that Alicia's reprieve could only be a short one; that the day would come when her husband would need her with an intensity and desperation that would drain her again and again, yet must still leave her overflowing with the love he craved but found so hard to ask for.

And when that happens, she thought, drawing him closer, I'll be there.

MORE ROMANCE FOR A SPECIAL WAY TO RELAX

$1.95 each

2 ☐ Hastings
3 ☐ Dixon
4 ☐ Vitek
5 ☐ Converse
6 ☐ Douglass
7 ☐ Stanford
8 ☐ Halston
9 ☐ Baxter
10 ☐ Thiels
11 ☐ Thornton
12 ☐ Sinclair
13 ☐ Beckman
14 ☐ Keene
15 ☐ James
16 ☐ Carr
17 ☐ John
18 ☐ Hamilton
19 ☐ Shaw
20 ☐ Musgrave
21 ☐ Hastings
22 ☐ Howard
23 ☐ Charles
24 ☐ Dixon
25 ☐ Hardy
26 ☐ Scott
27 ☐ Wisdom
28 ☐ Ripy
29 ☐ Bergen
30 ☐ Stephens
31 ☐ Baxter
32 ☐ Douglass
33 ☐ Palmer
35 ☐ James
36 ☐ Dailey
37 ☐ Stanford
38 ☐ John
39 ☐ Milan
40 ☐ Converse
41 ☐ Halston
42 ☐ Drummond
43 ☐ Shaw
44 ☐ Eden
45 ☐ Charles
46 ☐ Howard
47 ☐ Stephens
48 ☐ Ferrell
49 ☐ Hastings
50 ☐ Browning
51 ☐ Trent
52 ☐ Sinclair
53 ☐ Thomas
54 ☐ Hohl
55 ☐ Stanford
56 ☐ Wallace
57 ☐ Thornton
58 ☐ Douglass
59 ☐ Roberts
60 ☐ Thorne
61 ☐ Beckman
62 ☐ Bright
63 ☐ Wallace
64 ☐ Converse
65 ☐ Cates
66 ☐ Mikels
67 ☐ Shaw
68 ☐ Sinclair
69 ☐ Dalton
70 ☐ Clare
71 ☐ Skillern
72 ☐ Belmont
73 ☐ Taylor
74 ☐ Wisdom
75 ☐ John
76 ☐ Ripy
77 ☐ Bergen
78 ☐ Gladstone
79 ☐ Hastings
80 ☐ Douglass
81 ☐ Thornton
82 ☐ McKenna
83 ☐ Major
84 ☐ Stephens
85 ☐ Beckman
86 ☐ Halston